Danger and Romance in Foreign Lands

Stephen E. Eisenbraun

DORRANCE
PUBLISHING CO
EST. 1920
PITTSBURGH, PENNSYLVANIA 15238

Dorrance Publishing Co
585 Alpha Drive
Pittsburgh, PA 15238
Visit our website at www.dorrancebookstore.com

ISBN: 978-1-6376-4089-0
eISBN: 978-1-6376-4931-2

READER COMMENTS

"A compact tale that quickly hooks the reader with its fast-moving action and revealing cultural insights. It evokes times and places with a flair. Eisenbraun acquaints us with familiar cities of South Asia and East Africa but also with such exotic locales as Kashmir and Lamu Island, off the coast of Kenya. As the principal narrator, Scott is a journalist endowed with curiosity that uncovers great stories regarding historic events but also leads to nail-biting adventures, from encounters with threatening water buffalo to political intrigue. It reflects the assurance of a writer with experience to know whereof he speaks. And all of that set against a poignant romance makes this a memorable journey and satisfying page turner."

Jerome Hoganson
Veteran Foreign Service Officer & Refugee Program Director

"It was fun to be transported back to Mombasa with all the hustle and bustle … There was a definite sense of "place" that we especially liked, from the Club to the Old Town … and the feeling of threat in the weather—who could forget those black clouds massing and the oppressive heat? All the settings were good and plot twists exciting!

Janet and David Kite
British residents of Mombasa, Kenya, in the 1980s

"An American diplomat's nostalgic reverie into the past of postings in Pakistan, Bangladesh, India, and Kenya. The story escalates into a catching modern odyssey of cross-cultural romance, political events, and the decisive coming of age of South Asian women. Eisenbraun weaves a delicate tale through Scott, the journalist, and Rakhi, the sultry, attractive Indian banker. A pleasurable, magnetic read."

Shahnaz Wazir Ali,
Women's Rights Activist, Pakistan

"From South Asia to East Africa to London – a page-turning international romance sizzling and then unraveling against a backdrop of aircraft hijackings, failed military coups, the burning of a US Embassy, and the abduction of the Indian heroine. Eisenbraun writes a culturally sensitive account of the military and political brass he met and the adventures he experienced while in the Foreign Service but through the eyes of a foreign correspondent. His sharply observed stories will appeal to all lovers of travel, 'inter-cultural' affairs of the heart, and foreign intrigue. A woman-friendly book that delves into the pros and cons of marrying a foreigner, living abroad, and balancing marriage with professional ambitions."

Roberta Cohen,
Specialist in human rights and humanitarian issues
(whose career has spanned the United Nations, the State
Department, think tanks, NGOs, and academia)

Dedicated to Malik Wazir Ali and Nasra Wazir Ali,
Pakistani Patriots and Humanitarians Extraordinaire

I wish to thank my son, David J.B. Eisenbraun,
for his inspiration to write this story;
My wife Lorraine, who brought a critical eye to the text;
My daughter Annie, who made creative suggestions along the path; and
My daughter Sam for invaluable technical assistance.

And now again, this Memory's Book
Turns back the Pages, on Thoughts of Yore,
Those glistening Tears, that lingering Look
This Thirsting Heart, reft to the Core!

MIRZA GHALIB
Islamic Poet in the Court at Delhi
of the last of the Moghals
1794–1869
Translated by Sufia Sadullah

Part I

South Asia

Prologue

I am a man named Scott Higgins in my mid-seventies, but I look younger than my years, principally because I have been lucky with health and genetics. I teach history at Sweetbriar College, a small, private college for women. It is tucked into the wooded mountains of southern Virginia.

I am lucky there is a waiting list for those wishing to sign up for my classes, and I suspect that is so because I sprinkle my classes with stories of my younger days when I was a foreign correspondent, first in New Delhi, then in Nairobi, and later in London.

During my days in South Asia in the latter seventies, I was shot at while covering a story in Bangladesh, was almost burned alive by a furious mob in Pakistan, fell deeply in love with the most exquisite woman in New Delhi, and was the lucky recipient of friendship and affection from some of the most generous, kind, and attractive people one could ever know.

Before my memory fades, friends have encouraged me to record some of the experiences that have haunted me since my time in South Asia, notably the countries of India, Bangladesh, and Pakistan.

A New York-based newspaper hired me in 1977 to be posted as a junior foreign correspondent in India's capital, New Delhi, a city I was familiar with from my student days there some years earlier. I arrived during the summer monsoon, with the oppressive humidity and heat enough to send me straight back to the airport and a flight home, if I had not been so violently sick right off the bat with dysentery that I could not have crawled to the plane.

When I recovered sufficiently to hobble into the newspaper office, I was met with a sneer by the senior correspondent, Baxter, who may not have had a first name and who saw no reason for my posting in his office, where he had schemed to work year after year. There was no important politician in India he did not know intimately, and Baxter saw no purpose for my existence trolling over the same territory seeking out dispatches on internal politics. But Baxter had a solution that would get me, the greenhorn who might someday pick up information that would upstage him, out of sight and presumably out of trouble. I was to cover politics in Bangladesh, the new country to the east of India, and in Pakistan, the newly splintered country to the west of India.

What follows is a recounting of those dramatic years in South Asia, followed by an assignment to Nairobi and finally one in London. In 1977 when I joined the staff of the New York newspaper, I thought I could leave behind my small-town American, white privilege background and learn more about the larger world. My story shows that adventure, romance, and even danger is out there, waiting to find the one who least expects those matters to find him.

Chapter One

Arrival in Bangladesh

Hardly two weeks after my arrival in New Delhi, I was on a Thai International flight to Dhaka, the sprawling capital of the newly independent country of Bangladesh, the victor in a 1971 civil war that split the country of Pakistan.

But victor the new country of Bangladesh did not seem. First, looking out the airliner window as we approached Dhaka (or Dacca as the name was spelled then), I could not even see dry land, let alone any evidence of a city. There was nothing but rice fields filled knee-deep in water, with only clumps of trees here and there indicating a tiny farming village. A few one-lane roads with no traffic could be seen going nowhere. But the pilot did find an airstrip, and we landed at the decrepit sandstone-colored airport left over from the colonial era, and the mold-stained walls showed it had not likely been painted since those days that had ended thirty years previously. But it wasn't too hard to get through customs—much easier to get into Bangladesh than to exit India some hours before. And awaiting me was Ahmed, the local journalist who looked after our meager interests in the country while he pursued a pretty successful journalistic career. Or I should say he managed to know every one of importance in the city, even though because of strict press censorship, he could not write much about what he learned.

Ahmed took me to his rattletrap 1940s Morris, a serious luxury in a city whose public transport system then was dominated by bicycle rickshaws in the untold thousands. Slowly we made our way through rickshaws along tree-lined streets into the old commercial heart of the city, an area called Motijheel. Across from the broken-down building that housed the American Embassy on its fifth floor was the colonial-era Purbani Hotel, a hot and desolate structure that had never seen better days. But, it was dirt cheap and in the middle of the city, where political and commercial leaders could be reached by rickshaw. And the hotel was virtually within walking distance of the entrance to the old city, mostly defined as it had been for centuries by thick walls and narrow lanes. I did not know it then, but I would spend valuable time in the old city in the following year.

Like Delhi, Dacca was miserably hot and even more humid, and my hotel room had but a ceiling fan. That might have been adequate if the power could be trusted, but it failed for hours at a time every day, and most often at night. As I lay sweating in bed the first night, I had a good idea why old man Baxter had exiled me here. It was up to me, with Ahmed's help, to find out what was going on politically in the city and country and convey that to readers in the States, making my dispatches interesting enough for even just a few readers to pay attention.

In fact, Bangladesh had been born amidst terror and bloodshed during its war in 1971–72 with Pakistan, and then the country had been wracked by a famine that left millions starving. Add in political instability after the assassination of the first Prime Minister, Sheikh Mujibur (Mujib) Rahman, the hero of the revolution, and the new country was almost overwhelmed by the challenges it faced. When I arrived in 1977, the country had not recovered psychologically from the death of Sheikh Mujib, who wasn't just killed by a cadre of army majors on a steamy night in August 1975, his whole family had been massacred in a torrent of machine gun fire.

Now I was in the city just twenty-four months later, hoping to find politicians, students, businessmen, journalists, or anyone who could explain to me why such violence had occurred, and what was evolving in the post-Mujib era.

Chapter Two

A New Country

Although I had never been in Bangladesh physically before my arrival in August 1977, the country's tumultuous birth had been a vivid matter to me for a number of years. In my graduate school days studying international relations at Johns Hopkins, I had been consumed by the incredible story of the growth of Bangladeshi nationalism and the dynamism of Sheikh Mujib. I believed completely when it was said he could hold millions who hung on his every word because of the great charisma of his personality and the power of his words in Bengali, a language of great power and poetic beauty.

I was the only one at SAIS (as the Hopkins graduate program in international relations is known) at that time to take a serious interest in South Asia. I was also to my knowledge the only one at the school to hitchhike to New York City in early August, 1971, to attend The Concert for Bangladesh, a rock concert organized by Ravi Shankar, the Indian sitarist, and George Harrison, late of The Beatles, to raise money on behalf of the Bengali refugees fleeing East Pakistan and sheltering in the Indian state of West Bengal.

This became the first-ever rock concert organized for humanitarian purposes, although since that time, the world has seen many others. As Ravi Shankar said about this first event, the world did not know the name Bangla Desh (as it was spelled at first) until The Concert For Bangladesh helped increase awareness of the magnitude of human misery that had been under-reported in the western world. Shankar appealed to his friend, George Harrison, who invited many of his artistic friends to perform. The concert created quite a stir in America at the time with its all-star line-up that included former Beatles George Harrison and Ringo Starr, Bob Dylan, Eric Clapton, Leon Russell, and others who were moved to help the more than 10 million homeless refugees in India.

To Americans in 1971, Bangladesh/East Pakistan seemed so far away. Why were people starving to death there? What were they fighting for? These were some of the uninformed questions that Americans had in 1971 when the concert occurred. After the event, the music was made into a three-album boxed set and later a movie that was shown in theaters across America. Included were vivid photos and newsreels of suffering refugees in wretched camps. The photos and the music made the world aware of the crisis that had brought together top American rock, folk, gospel, and soul artists as well as Hindustani classical sitar-playing star Ravi Shankar to perform for charity. Ravi Shankar was born in India to a Bengali Brahman family and was devastated at the plight of the refugees fleeing East Pakistan for makeshift camps in the Indian state of West Bengal and in Calcutta itself, the capital of the state.

No account of my interest in Bangladesh and India would be complete from the period of my student days if I did not include my admiration of the Indian/Bengali poet Rabindranath Tagore, the first non-European to win in 1913 the Nobel Prize for Literature. I have read in English some of his poetry and also some of the novels he published in English. I also have been a life-long fan of the Bengali film maker Satyajit Ray, who was greatly influenced by Tagore. I have seen most of his films and attended a lecture he gave at the Kennedy Center in Washington. What many may not realize is that both Tagore and Ray explored the agony of love, and notably love's cousin, jealousy. They both did it in the context of painful love triangles. Someday in my college classes I will float my ideas on how much Ray was influenced by Tagore.

One cannot end mention of Tagore without noting that a portion of his poem "Amar Sonar Banga" (My Golden Bengal) forms the Bangladesh national anthem, and that a portion of another of his poems is the basis for the Indian national anthem.

Later that same fateful year of 1971 for events important to Bangladesh, I lucked out that in early November when Indian Prime

Minister Indira Gandhi came to Washington, I was able to hear her speak publicly. She had come to try to persuade the Nixon Administration to join her in putting pressure on Pakistan to relent in East Pakistan and let the eastern sector go its way.

As the world knows, she was unsuccessful. After meeting with President Nixon at the White House, she travelled up Massachusetts Avenue to the Washington National Cathedral to speak to the thousands of Indian nationals who had gathered at the cathedral. Because I had a friend on the staff of the Indian Embassy, I had a pass to join those assembled, and I think I was one of the few there who was not of South Asian background. Mrs. Gandhi solemnly addressed the thousands there who heard her make the case that India could not stand by idly with over ten million refugees in West Bengal, all of whom were desperate and hungry.

History reports that the U.S. continued to support Pakistan, and India declared war on Pakistan to force that country to back down in the east. The eastern sector gained its independence thanks to the Indian military intervention, but that freedom came at great bloodshed and sacrifice on the part of those who fought and did not flee the country.

Knowing this background, one can understand that I was excited to be in Dhaka with the opportunity to find those who could tell me of the dramatic events of the preceding years. If I was lucky and diligent, I might even find those who could explain what was happening in that summer of 1977. That story was harder to figure out than I thought it would be.

A triumvirate of generals had first assumed power in the months following Mujib's death, and by the time I arrived in 1977, the army chief, General Ziaur Rahman, had proclaimed himself Chief Martial Law Administrator and had imposed martial law, banning political activity and censoring the press. There was a nightly curfew strictly enforced by heavily armed soldiers at checkpoints, and in the day, no one could easily be found who felt free to talk about politics. Those few in the know were afraid to talk, and in truth, there wasn't much to be learned about underground political currents and plots. Or so I thought; it seemed to be a country without political activity, nor much commercial activity either in those first difficult years.

Chapter Three

The Dacca Party Scene

If it was hard to find anyone willing to talk politics (as opposed to explaining recent history, which everyone was anxious to relate to me and I was eager to hear), at night the city came alive. The bazaars teamed with activity, and far away from the city center the well-to-do in their surprisingly comfortable homes were partying, dancing to blaring disco music, guzzling alcohol, and flirting frantically, anxious it seemed to forget their daytime troubles with sexual escapades and marital drama.

How did I discover the late-night party scene? Through Ahmed, I got an invitation to a party only days after my arrival, and one social invitation led to another. Those partying the night away were the younger business and government leaders of the city. They gossiped with little regard for me, one of only a handful of expats invited. There was one young couple from the American Embassy (a young political officer named Steve who had a stylish wife, Jane), a Dutch diplomatic couple, and two Australian diplomats. That was it for foreign guests, and why I was included I never learned. At the many similar parties to come, the same handful of expats showed up. While we expats were too young to be important, the local men, all probably under forty, had significant positions in the new government or were in business. Their wives were extravagantly attractive and willing to flirt, even with me, a no-account foreigner.

I asked Ahmed, "Hey, how could such a wild party atmosphere exist in the middle of the desperate living circumstances for the millions in the city and countryside?"

Considering for a moment, he replied, "You know, it must be some kind of psychological release after so much death in the war and starvation in the years afterwards."

"You might be onto something profound, my friend. But is all the flirting real?"

"Oh, yes, and some marriages are crumbling," replied Ahmed. "General Zia recently exiled one ranking government official to a diplomatic post abroad because his affair was getting too steamy. Zia thought it was not good for his government's image."

In fact, one night, a married local woman with a husband in a prominent government position, settled next to me and commented, "You're a newcomer in this city. You don't know that women here have certain needs, and we know how to satisfy them."

I tried to be casual, "Does it work?" was my strange response.

"Yes, come around to my friend's house tomorrow afternoon, and you will learn our ways." I let that invitation hang in the air with a lame comment, "That might be nice sometime," and then excused myself to find a drink.

The most extravagant host in those days was a well-to-do, dashing businessman named Aziz Mohammad Bhai. His parties in that era may still be legendary in Bangladesh to this day. Aziz, who in later years when I met him again in Dhaka, had come to resemble physically the Scottish actor Sean Connery. Aziz had a yellow antique Rolls Royce, which he occasionally drove around the city. It was a bit of a contrast with the rickshaws.

Let me add that Aziz was the host for the American heavyweight boxer Mohammad Ali, who came to Bangladesh several times in the late 1970s. You remember his motto, "Float like a butterfly, sting like a bee!" In fact, I bumped into Ali on his visit to Bangladesh in April 1978. I too was visiting and was at the airport VIP lounge picking up old man Baxter coming in from Delhi when Ali was departing. Although I did not meet Ali personally (I was too shy to say hello in the small VIP lounge), I could see how much of a beating he had received a week or two earlier when he had been defeated by Leon Spinks. Ali's face was still distorted. I should add that Ali was in Bangladesh to put on a number of boxing matches with local boxers. He was a goodwill ambassador, especially for coming to Dacca immediately after his defeat, and in spite of his defeat.

Meaningless gossip was all I overheard at the several parties I attended in that first two-week visit to Dacca. Nothing worth reporting to readers in Washington ever developed. It really did seem that a country so recently born in violence had clammed up under the no-nonsense eye of General Zia and the ever-present army, an organization totally absent from the parties I attended. What the officers and enlisted men did socially I never learned. But many weren't sleeping at night, I discovered soon enough.

Chapter Four

Japanese Aircraft Hijacking

On a subsequent visit to Dacca in late September, while I was travelling around by rickshaw to meet shady characters in greasy Chinese restaurants to whisper about nothing of consequence, terrorists of the outlawed Japanese Red Army were plotting the hijacking of a large Japanese airliner in the region. The aircraft was a DC-8 bound for Bangkok from Bombay, with 156 passengers. The hijackers took over the plane with the intent of forcing it to fly, I suppose, somewhere important, such as New Delhi or Bangkok, where the world's press would be available to hear the hijackers' demands for the release of their comrades in Japanese prisons. But as I understood later, no airport in India would allow the plane to land, and getting short of fuel, the plane desperately descended into Dacca, catching the country and subsequently the world by utter surprise.

The airliner remained tightly closed on the airport tarmac, while the terrorists on board demanded six million U.S. dollars, fuel to depart, and nine comrades in Japanese prisons. If there was no immediately positive response, there would be deaths of those aboard, the terrorists announced, and the world learned quickly that there were a number of prominent American tourists on board. They were singled out with threatened death.

When I heard about the landing of the Japanese aircraft, I hurried to the airport, expecting a quick resolution to the episode. Quickly all of Dacca learned about the hijacking, and amazingly fast, a television camera was set up to show the plane on the tarmac. An open radio channel was established to communicate with the hijackers, who spoke some

English. The minister of aviation, Air Vice Marshal AVM Mahmoud, set up a command post in the control tower to negotiate. What he wanted was the safe release of all passengers before fuel would be provided for the plane. The talks dragged on for several days. I napped sporadically on the floor in the corner of the small arrival terminal. Vice Marshal Mahmoud did not sleep, it seemed, as he patiently talked with the increasingly restive hijackers. And astonishingly, all of the city heard the negotiations. I never learned why the Bangladesh authorities allowed the talks to be on the public radio station.

I would like to say I learned the inside story of the negotiations from contacts at the airport. In fact, I learned all the vital information from listening to the radio, as did seemingly all of the country. I was the only foreign newspaperman in the airport, and I did my best to telephone the unfolding story to Ahmed, who relayed it to New York.

The hijackers demanded that the Japanese government release specific Japanese Red Army comrades in Japan and transport them to Dacca. To my astonishment, the Japanese did just that, and a Japanese plane landed the next day, supposedly with the released prisoners. The rumor at the airport was that the plane was packed with commandos to storm the commercial aircraft still on the tarmac. The Vice Marshal, so I heard, firmly kept control of the situation, and the aircraft was isolated a mile away at the end of a runway. We learned at dawn of the third day that there were some released prisoners on the aircraft when a few were exchanged for exhausted American tourists. I never learned whether there were commandos on the distant plane and eventually it did not matter.

Chapter Five

Air Force Enlisted Men Mutiny

At dawn on the third day of the hijacking drama I was abruptly ripped from slumber in the smelly airport terminal by rifle shots around me. Staggering to my feet, I saw men in uniform shooting their way through the small terminal and heading for the stairs leading to the control tower. Dropping fast to the floor, I crawled to hide under a wooden table. A young officer from the American Embassy sheltered there too.

"What the fuck?" he said.

I think he was expressing surprise at the armed attack, but equally he could have been angered by my pushing with him under the table.

"What now?" I asked, breathless.

"Just keep your head down!"

I could hear more shots, this time from an automatic weapon, coming from above, presumably from the nearby control tower.

"Shit, that's where Mahmoud is!" muttered the American.

At that moment, the Air Vice Marshal's voice could be heard on the radio calling to the terrorists: "Be informed that strangers with weapons are in the airport. They are not friendly. Protect yourselves." Then radio silence.

While we crouched under the table, more excited soldiers ran through the terminal, and then others appeared.

"Look, other soldiers are arriving!" I had barely said this when the new arrivals started a firefight with the original soldiers.

"What the hell is going on?" exclaimed my American companion. "Soldiers fighting soldiers?"

More gunfire came from above us, presumably from the control tower. The American had a hand-held radio, which came to life. An

Embassy officer was saying for us to keep sheltering; a mutiny by air force enlisted men seemed to have broken out.

The terrorists, still on the plane, could be heard shouting, "What's happening?" With no answer, the plane's engines started, and the craft turned in a tight circle and gunned away from the terminal. I glanced out a nearby fly-speckled window to see the plane streaking down the tarmac to assume a position for takeoff. Simultaneously, several fire-trucks zoomed to block the takeoff route.

A Bangladeshi voice, not that of the Vice Marshal, ordered the Japanese plane to return to the terminal. There really was no choice, since fuel still had not been transferred, to say nothing about the equipment blocking the runway. The Japanese plane slowly rolled back to the terminal. The unfamiliar voice on the radio commanded the hijackers to nose in close to the terminal, clearly thwarting any further escape.

The arriving soldiers poured into the terminal and very quickly established order with no more shooting. The new negotiator began to work quickly with the hijackers on the plane to trade passengers for fuel and Japanese prisoners brought from Tokyo. Apparently the two sides had reached an accord: The hijacked plane was a distraction to the Bangladesh military in light of what seemed a failed military coup, and the Japanese wanted to get away fast from a dangerous situation they could not control.

It seemed to me there was no more breaking news at the airport, so I dashed into the parking lot, where Ahmed was waiting with his old Minor, and we drove to the nearby Intercon Hotel, where released passengers were being sheltered. I found a stylish American woman, middle-aged, willing to talk to me for a few minutes.

"I never thought I would end up a pawn in a terrorist plot!" she exclaimed.

"My husband is tight with top political leaders in California, and they are going to know what a hero the American Ambassador is for negotiating our safe release!" Then she was off to a room provided by the hotel. She never explained how the Ambassador had pulled off his diplomatic success.

I lingered in the luxury hotel lobby for some hours, hoping to find more released hostages to interview, and composing a dispatch to New York, copying Baxter in New Delhi. Then just after sunset in the growing twilight, the plane was pushed back from the terminal. We watched on an ancient black and white monitor set up in the lobby as the plane raced down the runway. It was almost too dark to see it lift off for some unknown destination. The plane did get full of fuel and with all dozen or so Japanese Red Army former prisoners on board. We understood a few Americans were still held captive as bargaining chips at some destination unknown to us.

We heard subsequently the plane made its way to Algiers, where Algerian authorities greeted warmly the hijackers and released the last Americans. The question on my mind was what had happened to the Vice Marshal. It was weeks later, long after my return to New Delhi, that I heard about a dozen ranking air force officers were killed, most in the control tower, but that the Vice Marshal was not among them.

Vice Marshal Mahmoud was gone from the scene just after attaining hero status for his remarkable negotiating skills. But, after all, it turned out to have been a failed military coup led mostly by air force enlisted men under Mahmoud's command. At the time, I could not learn of Mahmoud's status, but a good many air force and perhaps some army personnel were summarily hanged by Zia a few months after the short-lived mutiny. I should stress that no one knows for certain what happened, in that no press or other outside observers covered what were thought on the gossip circuit in Dacca to be virtual kangaroo court trials that almost always ended up in the accused being hanged. But I never heard if Mahmoud was caught up in the violence. Years later on another trip to Dacca, then called Dhaka, Ahmed told me Mahmoud was living quietly in retirement in the city.

Ahmed arranged for me to have tea with Mahmoud one afternoon. To my question about events in the control tower that dangerous morning, he replied calmly, "Well, about six of us were lined up against the wall by the sepoys (the enlisted men) and were shot individually. When they came to me, someone said, 'He is a good man! Leave him!'"

Chapter Six

A Soviet Embassy Approach

Every year in those days, Iranian Embassies worldwide threw a grand affair for the Iranian national day. It was the reception of all receptions, but it was not exclusive in that everyone of even remote social standing in the host capital city would be invited, or so I thought. Even in Bangladesh, there must have been well over a thousand guests at the outdoor evening affair that served the finest of foods and drinks. Even I as an occasional journalist in the city received an invitation, which I accepted gratefully because I knew it would be a priceless opportunity to meet those of significance in Dacca.

I was surrounded at the reception by hundreds of diplomats but not as many Bangladeshis as I had hoped. It seems the Iranians may not have known or cared who was important in the Bangladesh community but spent lavishly to entertain the entire diplomatic corps in the capital. I had no idea there were so many embassies in Dacca, and I wondered what all those young diplomats did on a daily basis.

I wasn't alone for long in the sea of people I did not know. A handsome and friendly fellow with a charming wife introduced himself as Vladimir, first secretary of the Soviet embassy. His wife Natasha also greeted me warmly.

"What do you do in Dacca?" Vladimir asked.

"Well, I'm actually visiting from Delhi as a correspondent."

If there was a momentary hint of surprise and perhaps disappointment on Vladimir's face, it vanished instantly, skilled as he was in social matters. He said I looked like the young second secretary Steve at the American Embassy.

"Oh, I didn't realize Soviets and Americans socialized in Dacca," I replied.

"No, that is true, but it is time old patterns are broken," he replied. "But you are American, and I don't encounter too many Americans here who are not working for their government."

Going on, Vladimir said "Why don't you come around for dinner sometime soon? Natasha and I would like to get to know you."

We set up a plan for dinner at Vladimir and Natasha's small flat a few nights hence. I was a bit apprehensive. What good could come from knowing a Soviet?

The next day, I went around to the American Embassy and paid a call on Steve, the young political officer the Soviet had mistaken for me. Steve, who surprisingly had not been at the reception, was astonished to hear I had been approached by a Soviet Embassy official and invited to dinner with him and his wife. He was also more than surprised that the Soviet had mentioned his name.

"Inviting a foreigner to a Soviet embassy home is never done without explicit prior permission, no doubt from Moscow" he explained. "Dacca may seem a world far removed from the Cold War drama elsewhere in the world, but it is very much alive here. Why do you think there is a large Soviet Embassy in Bangladesh? Certainly not to cultivate Bangladeshis. It is to get to know, and maybe recruit, an American official, or perhaps another Western diplomat."

Steve said he would check out Vladimir and get back to me. In the meantime, he urged me to accept the social invitation to at least see what was up. He wanted me to return and report what transpired.

Soon after, I had a pleasant evening at the Soviet home, with good Russian food and wine, with American jazz on the up-to-date stereo. Vladimir and Natasha seemed to be at ease and I relaxed accordingly. The talk evolved into a discussion of the freedom I enjoyed, notably for foreign travel. My hosts drew a stark contrast with their restricted life. I noted I was heading off to Bangkok in a few days just for fun. Vladimir and Natasha were envious.

"If only we could travel like that!" Natasha said. "We are confined to Dacca and never receive permission to leave. You are so lucky!" That theme replayed itself as the evening grew longer. At its conclusion, Vladimir invited me to his embassy the following Friday night, adding that the staff had regular parties every Friday.

Next day I returned to the American Embassy, where I met Steve and an older political officer named Fred, a friendly guy. Fred confirmed that Vladimir was a KGB officer, and the mere fact that he was so fluent in English and had the privilege of living off the Soviet compound, which was ringed with a high wall with barbed wire pointing inward, was further evidence that he was not an ordinary embassy staffer. They urged me to accept the Soviet embassy invitation, adding that no American embassy staffer had ever been in the Soviet embassy, much less to a party.

I went around on the next Friday night. A large indoor reception room was filled with at least a hundred embassy staffers—no Bangladeshis and certainly no other expats. I met many of the embassy senior staff, all of whom seemed to know my name. My hosts plied me with cold shots of vodka, and they watched with concern that I tried merely to sip the drinks, whereas they knocked them back time and again. It wasn't long before a ranking fellow from across the room shouted pointedly to me, "Scott, Nastrovia!" and downed his vodka. I had no choice but to do the same, and the cold liquid felt quite good as it hit my stomach and warmed my innards.

There was pulsing Western music, and everyone was dancing wildly, drinking heavily. It seemed the point was to get as drunk as possible as quickly as possible. A pretty Russian girl appeared, took my hand, and started to dance with me. It was fun, but I did my best to remain as sober as I could.

Vladimir grabbed my arm after a while and firmly led me to a corner. He mentioned that President Carter had given a major speech a few days previously, and Vladimir asked if I could find a copy of the speech for him. Puzzled that he did not have it, I nonetheless agreed to try to find a copy.

A few days later I went again to the U.S. Embassy and reported about the party. Fred said he had no doubt the Russians were interested in developing me as a potential recruit for them. Fred wanted me to introduce him to Vladimir, but I declined.

I knew Baxter back in Delhi would think I was a fool to get mixed up with Soviets, and I was a bit afraid to continue, so I conveniently returned to Delhi and on subsequent trips did not make any attempt to contact my so-called Russian friend.

I wonder to this day whether there is a file on me in Moscow, a file stamped "waste of time."

Chapter Seven

A Lost Winter Weekend in London

It was lonesome socially to hang around Delhi that first winter and shuttle to Bangladesh, with an occasional trip to Pakistan interspersed. There simply weren't many single women in my New Delhi world, and I was rootless anyway with all the regional travel. I heard there was a fun social scene in New Delhi among the expats, but I was not in town enough to become an active part of it.

I did have a pleasant social experience, however, one night at a dinner given by a British couple I had met. The function had been well underway when in came Nasreen with another Indian couple. I made it a point to chat with her, which was a delightful matter. She was in town visiting her sister for a few days. Nasreen prided herself on being single and successful in London, where she worked by day at a London publishing house and by night as the hostess of a Lebanese restaurant near Cambridge Circle in the theater district. The restaurant, Nasreen told me, was the toast of the Arab community in London. Later I discovered with Nasreen that the food was indeed superb.

That first night, I cannot remember talking with anyone but Nasreen. From the first moment that evening, we seemed to be old friends. It didn't hurt that, like most of the Indian women from the upper classes, she was pretty with gorgeous thick black hair. She was slender but well-endowed, provocatively dressed, spoke perfect English, was conversant about political matters, and had an easy manner with men. When she was in town, I took her out to dinner a few times. The truth is, there was almost nowhere to go on a date but a few modest restaurants. She stayed with her sister, so seeing her at her sister's was out of the question. I did not suggest my place, which was sparsely furnished though in a nice neighborhood.

One cold evening in January 1978, Nasreen asked by long-distance phone if I wanted to visit her in London. She said she would meet me at Heathrow airport, and we could have a long weekend seeing the sights of the town. I booked a non-stop, red-eye flight to London, without even knowing her residential address, and I had forgotten to ask for her telephone number.

I arrived very early in the morning at Heathrow; no Nasreen around. I waited over an hour, spirits flagging. Finally, I decided to take a taxi into town, but just as I was about to leave the terminal, a public announcement popped up with my name and telling me to contact the information desk. I made my way there and found a message with Nasreen's number.

"Hello?" She answered. "I'm so sorry I couldn't get to the airport, but I needed to borrow a car and my plan fell through at the last moment. Meet me at Victoria station."

I took an expensive taxi into the rail station, marveling that only a few more moments at the air terminal and I would not have gotten the message. It would have been a lonely weekend in London. I arrived at Victoria station; no Nasreen.

I waited another hour, growing increasingly irritated and cold in the unheated train station. What was with this girl? But I didn't give up, and eventually she appeared, all apologies. Seeing her cheered me up considerably because she gave me an affectionate kiss and said she would make up for her tardiness. I vividly recall her dark blue woolen dress and black high heels. *Wasn't she unduly fancy for mid-morning on Saturday?* I thought to myself. The effect was alluring, especially for a guy coming to the Western world after months in South Asia, where women's legs were never revealed.

The first order of business was to find breakfast after my overnight flight.

"I know a cozy place in my neighborhood. Let's go there and then on to my flat." Another taxi ride ensued, and it became costly as we ventured into a residential neighborhood.

After a satisfying British breakfast of eggs, bacon, baked beans, and fried tomatoes, which Nasreen watched me consume while only sipping coffee, we headed to her nearby two-room flat. There was just a sitting room with a pullout bed attached to an old sofa, and a kitchen, plus a tiny bathroom.

Hardly in the door, she kissed me again and said, "Let's have a drink."

She mixed a gin and tonic and put some pleasing music on her stereo, starting with Van McCoy's "The Hustle," a favorite of mine from that era. Soon there was a blue woolen dress on the floor, and the whole day we did not leave the pullout bed. I did not see the tourist sights of London that day, nor that weekend.

In the evening we went to a Lebanese restaurant near her flat. I was in the greatest of spirits, but she was a bit wary of the atmosphere in the restaurant. She said there were patrons, almost all Arab, who were giving her unfriendly looks, and she knew why. They were shooting thoughts to her, such as, *why are you with a Westerner? Stick to your own culture.* I was blithely unaware of such undertones but was sorry Nasreen was less comfortable than she had been during the day.

The next night Nasreen invited me to her restaurant in Cambridge Circle, even though she was working that night as the hostess. I dined alone and watched her from a distance as she graciously met new patrons, a mixture of Arabs and British.

Sometime after midnight, and after more drinks than I needed as I waited for her, Nasreen closed the restaurant and said, "Let's go gambling! I feel lucky tonight!" She looked sexy and animated, and maybe that would translate into good luck. Her eyes were particularly bright and dancing.

"Okay, but I don't want to lose what little money I have left, and I depart early in the morning back to Delhi."

"Don't worry about tomorrow. The Playboy Club is nearby, and they know me there. It will be fun!"

Turns out they indeed did know Nasreen well, and we had not the slightest trouble walking in, although she was not a member and there was a line of those hopeful to gain entrance. She headed straight to the roulette tables while I was immediately offered a free drink from a most gorgeous woman in a bunny costume. Then I accepted another drink. *God, the bunnies at the club were out of this world. Where did the club find them?* To me, people watching, in least in this pleasing environment, was more fun than gambling. I knew I would lose, anyway, so why chance it?

In forty-five minutes, Nasreen reappeared, distraught, shaky, and glassy-eyed. She wasn't the same cheerful girl. She caught my arm roughly and demanded breathlessly, "Give me a hundred pounds! My luck went bad, but I can feel it is coming back, even though I am out of money!" Her tone had a harsh edge that was not nice.

"I don't even have a hundred pounds on me," I replied.

She continued to plead to no avail. Then her tone changed, and she spit out, "You're just a cheap bastard journalist. Of course, you don't have any money! I'm headed back to the restaurant to open the safe."

"Look, you can't rob the restaurant safe. That's crazy!" I protested.

"Get out of my way."

"No, I'll come with you to talk you out of it."

Once on the sidewalk in the cool late-night air, her demeanor suddenly reverted to the more normal one I recognized, and she said, wearily, "Let's just go home; I'm tired and bored." She motioned for a taxi, and I simply followed her. Her flat that night was a strange and cold place that I could not wait to leave.

The trip alone to the airport the next morning was a sour affair.

Chapter Eight

The Old City of Dacca

My visits to Dacca became more infrequent in the winter of 1977–78, partly because I could find so little of political interest to report. General Zia really was effective in keeping a lid on overt political activities, and it wasn't easy to learn about any covert activity, if it even existed. I hit on a way to get a little color into my occasional reporting, and gain historical perspective, by looking up much older political leaders who I was told were retired from the current scene.

Ahmed was of great assistance. The very first elderly gentleman he put me in touch with was Jadu Mia, a leader from the 1950s who had been associated with an even older and deceased politician, Badshah Khan, casually known in his day as the "Frontier Gandhi." In fact, Jadu Mia was a nickname meaning "magic man." His real name was Mashiur Rahman.

I had to take a bicycle rickshaw into the old city of Dacca. The lanes were too narrow and crowded to allow any other form of transport. I found the house, somehow, and had to climb a flight of steps to the third level, where I found the old man sitting on a narrow balcony overlooking the teeming street. He was smoking a hookah. He looked tired and rumpled, as though he had just gotten out of bed and had not changed clothes, nor shaved in three days. Still, his eyes were lively, and I think he was flattered that a youngster knew his name and wanted to talk politics with him.

Over chai, we reviewed the current political scene.

"What is your impression of General Zia?" I asked at one point.

"I think he is a good man in an impossible position. You know, he did not seek power in 1975; political leaders came to him one night in the cantonment and asked him to take over after the bloody chaos in the months following the assassination of Mujib."

"Since that time, he has turned into a national leader. Do you see how he travels all around the country, walking through villages and learning the problems of the ordinary man and woman? He is just what the country needs. The reception he receives in the countryside is quite friendly."

In like manner, we reviewed the older figures on the political scene. I stress older, because so many of the younger leaders from the 1971 war for independence had been killed in the war or were in self-imposed exile. What few were around seemed to keep a very low profile.

"What this country needs is a viable alternative to the Awami League." He was referring to the political party of Bangladesh independence that had been led by the assassinated Sheikh Mujibur Rahman.

We spent an enjoyable hour together. I departed with a new perspective on General Zia and the challenges facing his leadership. The venture to look up politicians of an earlier era was off to a good start.

A few days later a young boy, maybe twelve, showed up early in the morning at the Purbani Hotel lobby with a verbal message from Jadu Mia. I was supposed to come back to the old city as soon as I could for another chat. I grabbed a rickshaw.

The man who had recently received me on his balcony and drawing from his hookah was a changed man from just days earlier. He was clean shaven, and he was wearing fresh white kurta/pajamas. There was a sparkle in his eye with no hint as before of having just awakened.

He got right to the reason for summoning me back to the old city.

"General Zia is searching for a way to create a political party of his own. He summoned me at midnight to the cantonment to discuss how to form a political party, and who should be its leaders. But this is secret; you can't tell anyone."

"But why tell me? I'm a journalist. I write for the public. This sounds like a good story."

"Because Zia wants the accurate inside story known of how his new party is being created. There will come a time when you can tell the world. But I vouched for your discretion now, so don't disappoint me."

I agreed to his terms. If what Jadu Mia was describing came to pass, it was going to be a major story.

"Zia wants his new party to represent all of Bangladesh, not just those from the Awami League with its close ties to India."

"What are you going to call the new party? And did anyone else attend the meeting in the cantonment?"

"We haven't settled on a name, and I was the first Zia contacted. We will invite representatives from the left and the right, and especially from the Islamic world, which feels left out of the Awami League."

Jadu Mia promised to keep in touch, and I said I would look him up as soon as I returned to the country in a few weeks. We both kept our word. We met again in a few weeks.

"We're going to call the new party the Bangladesh Nationalist Party. And we already have a party constitution," Jadu Mia added with pride.

"Who wrote it?"

"A young barrister named Moudud Ahmed." I made a note to look him up.

We had several more meetings that extended through the latter part of June. Jadu Mia kept feeding me specific information. I finally had Old Baxter's attention in Delhi. "Jadu Mia must have permission from Zia to pass all this info to you. Maybe he thinks a journalist is neutral, as opposed to an embassy source. Keep listening."

Our last meeting was probably in the third week of June 1978. Jadu Mia named those who would be in a national cabinet, and he said Zia would allow open politicking in the country for parliamentary elections later in the year. I noticed that Jadu Mia did not name a chief minister, and that he himself was not in the cabinet. I asked him why.

"Oh, I'm too old to be in politics again," he replied with a twinkle in his eye. "But I will tell you who gets to be chief minister at our next meeting."

The following day, just as I was preparing to head to the airport for the Thai flight to Delhi, I picked up a newspaper to read the banner headline about Zia's naming a cabinet and calling for parliamentary elections. Jadu Mia was Chief Minister. Zia would continue as self-appointed president. I did not, however, get to congratulate my new friend and confidante.

I never saw Jadu Mia again, although my dispatch on the development of the new political party and the announcement of coming elections in Bangladesh got good play Stateside, and the editors thanked me for my old-fashioned gumshoe reporting. Even old Baxter acknowledged I had finally achieved a scoop as a result of real journalistic effort, not just being lucky.

I did not, however, return to Bangladesh for quite some time. Instead, I was pulled back to do some feature reporting in India, and then I got involved in reporting Pakistani developments, which had taken a dramatic turn. I read that Jadu Mia died of a stroke in March of 1979. The Bangladesh Nationalist Party, popularly known as the BNP, became a going concern. The man who drafted the party constitution, Moudud Ahmed, rose to be Prime Minister in 1988 and Vice President from September 1989 to December 1990. But I was no longer in South Asia then and only read about these developments in the international press.

The life of a journalist is a transitory thing. I am getting ahead of myself; there is still much to tell about my posting in New Delhi and my growing focus on Pakistan.

Chapter Nine

Delhi University

My boss Baxter pulled me back to Delhi after so much time in Bangladesh. Baxter grudgingly acknowledged I had comported myself well when caught up in the dramatic events there, but I think he saw my reporting as the product of being in the right place at the right time, to use an old cliché, and not the result of any inherent skill on my part to develop contacts and break a story. I was sorry to leave Dacca. It was exotic to ride rickshaws through the city, especially in the evening when all one could hear was the gentle tinkle of the rider's bells, and to see the bobbing lanterns on the back axles of the rickshaws. I will always remember also the majestic thunderheads that would darken the sky during the rainy season. What I witnessed was worthy of great poetry.

Baxter thought there was a story to be unearthed on the university campuses in the Delhi area. And since I was barely thirty and a former student at Delhi University, he thought it would be only natural that I hang around the several campuses in the city, get to know students, and find a scoop.

"You were a student at Delhi University, right?" Baxter asked.

"Yes. I was studying Hindi under a fellowship, and the language study was part of my master's degree program in international relations at Johns Hopkins. I didn't learn too much Hindi, but I absorbed invaluable insights into the Indian culture that year." Baxter had no response to this bit of personal history. He probably thought my "invaluable" comment was overstated.

I headed out to the main Delhi University campus on the then outskirts of the sprawling city. A trip there meant traversing from New

Delhi into the crowded old city with its narrow lanes and the majestic Red Fort and mosque from the days of the Mogul Empire, and thereafter continuing through what the British colonials called Civil Lines, a pleasant leafy residential area popular with the British colonials. Beyond Civil Lines, one continued along Mall Road, which was also the Delhi portion of the Grand Trunk Road that ran from Calcutta to the border with Pakistan and onward through Pakistan to the Khyber Pass on the border with Afghanistan.

I loved that congested road from my student days when I lived adjacent to it; one might encounter someone riding an elephant, or a caravan of camels heading to the nearby countryside, and always there would be a vast number of horse-drawn carts with sweating horses straining to pull their carts. There were frightening lorries—that is, seriously overcrowded trucks—that careened along the road, the drivers blasting air horns instead of using brakes, ploughing through the traffic that also included a good number of white cows, oblivious to the din of the horns as they pursued their separate agendas.

As I approached the campus, maybe a short mile off Mall Road, I was not surprised to find that the Tibetan refugee camp with its thousands of inhabitants was still there. They had fled Tibet in the 1950s and 1960s to escape repression from the Beijing government of the People's Republic of China. In my student days, a campus friend had taken me into the camps to sample the food in the tiny food stalls where all the truck drivers, as well as the occasional university student, frequented. Kar had introduced me to what was known in the camp as pork chou chou, a curried pork with vegetables ladled over rice. It was fresh, hot, very tasty, and within a student's budget, costing maybe three rupees, which then was about 50 cents. I was tempted to stop again, but I passed on.

On campus, I headed to the main building of the Delhi School of Economics, where I knew from the old days I would likely find a few dusty coffeehouses with students lounging around. To say coffeehouse was a misnomer; in fact, the area was just a few benches or plastic chairs in the dirt under a tree, with a small grubby interior area for sitting, but most students preferred to sit outside where it was cooler, although that was a relative concept. It was always excruciatingly hot except for a short six weeks in December through mid-January. Sure enough, there were students around, just as I remembered. The Delhi School was a graduate program in economics and political science. The students were, they were quick to tell me, the most sophisticated in all of India, and smart as hell. The latter was certainly true.

I sauntered up and asked for a cup of chai (tea with milk and lots of sugar). The Indian students eyed me suspiciously at first, but their natural friendliness and curiosity got the best of them, which I had counted on. Within minutes, a few students gathered around.

"What are you doing here?" someone asked.

"I'm just revisiting old haunts; I was a student here once and took a few courses in international trade theory."

"No one takes just a few courses here. You're either a serious full-time student or you're not."

"True, I was actually studying Hindi elsewhere on the campus and got permission to audit a class." I mentioned the professor's name, which caught their attention, because he was a legend at the school and had also taught at MIT.

"But why would you be studying Hindi?" my skeptical new friend asked. "Why here?" he went on. "All of us aspire to study in America, so why would you, presumably an American, want to waste your time on this campus?"

The group of five or six around me nodded in agreement. They were not really unfriendly, just suspicious of my presence. No foreigners ever ventured so far from the tourist and business areas of the city.

"In fact," he went on, answering his own question. "There can be only one reason for your showing up here; you're a spy."

I had gotten this response years ago when I was a student and was not surprised that that old chestnut was still being trotted out.

"Do you really think the American government gives a damn about what happens on this campus, or believes that India's national secrets are being discussed in class?" I asked, gesturing to the building above us. "I'm just a journalist trying to learn something about current life in India."

They laughed in agreement about the national secrets crack, and the tension immediately evaporated.

"But," I stated, "one thing I see that is the same as it was years ago here: the female students are as stunningly beautiful as ever. In fact, how can it be that Miranda House girls are all potential Miss India contestants?"

That we could all agree on. I asked about Eve-teasing, the practice so prevalent on campus years ago of verbally harassing the female students. The guys at the coffeehouse said it was a sport all enjoyed, including the girls.

"I can't believe they enjoy it. There is no woman around here, and perhaps that's why," I observed. I assumed as in the old days that the female students segregated themselves, always walking on campus in groups, presumably for self-protection.

"Oh, it's all harmless."

And so went my conversation. I didn't bring up national political issues, nor did they. Baxter's theory did not get validated that day regarding the campuses as hotbeds of politics, but in truth I did not try to find answers. I did do a feature on Eve-teasing. The practice was not confined to university campuses; women were subjected to verbal abuse constantly on the streets, and also physical molestation in most public venues, especially while riding buses.

What was then a nuisance grew over the years to be a human rights issue nationally in India, when Eve-teasing turned into rape in some notorious cases. I understand the issue now has the world's attention, judging from human rights reporting by global non-governmental organizations and coverage in the U.S. Department of State's human rights reports.

Chapter Ten

Adventures in Bombay, Madras, and Calcutta

The next several months I spent travelling around India, seeking out feature stories. There was also a short trip over to Lahore, Pakistan, to report on the growing dissatisfaction with the President, Zulfikar Ali Bhutto, who had incurred the dislike of the Muslim majority, which was particularly restive in Lahore, the capital of the Punjab province, the political heart and historical soul of the country. The mullahs could send out the word and produce an angry crowd of thousands of young men in the streets within an hour, and the police could do nothing about it. I knew Pakistan was going to play a major role in my life in the coming two years.

In the meantime, at a dinner in Lahore I met a friendly young couple. The wife, upon hearing that I was soon to visit Bombay, gave me the name of her cousin (I think she was a cousin—some family connection anyway) who was the wife of one of Bombay's film producers.

Soon after arriving in Bombay, I gave the wife, Navid, a call. When she heard I was a friend of her Lahore cousin, Navid said immediately, "Come to dinner tonight! We're having a little get together, and Shireen, in from Kashmir, will be there! You can't pass up a chance to meet her!" My dinner plans were made, just like that.

I asked around during the day about Shireen, since Navid had planted in my mind that Shireen was somebody special.

"Shireen?" An elderly journalist exclaimed as I interviewed him at his one-room apartment high above the Malabar Hills and featuring a giant open window, no glass, shutter, or screen, looking out over the city. "My boy, she is without doubt the most seductive woman in the world. No man can resist her smile! But she is not in films, so much the pity. She is the producer's sister and lives in Srinagar, the capital city of Kashmir, which you can't ignore," he added. "It is a tourist's paradise with its cool mountain air and beautiful lake." Little could I guess that within a year I would be having tea with Shireen at her attractive and spacious home in Srinagar.

That night, I took a taxi to the producer's home in Silver Beach, far north of Bombay. There were just a few guests, a debonair guy I learned was an actor, and two women besides Navid, the producer's wife. Yes, Shireen was arresting, as I had been led to believe. But like most unusually attractive women the world round, she had a cool reserve and paid me little heed. The other female guest, an attractive woman in perhaps her late thirties, wore a white dress with a flowing skirt and a sleeveless top. It was a copy, I am certain, of Marilyn Monroe's famous white dress featured in her film *The Seven Year Itch*. What man would not remember that dress billowing to her waist as she stood over the subway grate in New York City?

It was my good fortune that the woman in white found it worthwhile to chat at length with me. I asked her what she did.

"Oh, I've made a few films, but not too many nowadays."

"So, what do you do now?" I asked.

"I am very choosy about film roles. And I am more interested in politics, frankly," she said. That suited me fine, since that was a topic I knew fairly well. We reviewed the political scene in India, discussed regional politics, and even relations between India and the United States. She was well-informed and thoughtful; more so, in fact, than many of the tiresome politicians and other political observers I had been interviewing who wanted mostly to explain the history of their country and their party for the past fifty years.

I hardly talked with anyone else at the party that night, and we agreed to meet again so I might do a profile of her. We set a date for lunch a few days later at the Taj Mahal hotel, a majestic structure built to resemble a Mogul fort and dominating the harbor waterfront. Not a place a young journalist could afford, but because I was staying at the

Salvation Army hostel just behind the grand hotel, I figured my finances would balance even if I splurged on a luncheon my office might not reimburse. My patronage of the hostel behind the hotel did not come up at the luncheon.

Heads turned when we entered the restaurant. The host of the elegant café with a flourish gave us the best table with a fine view of the harbor. Some of the other patrons, mostly stylish Indian women, looked my guest over carefully as we were seated. She wore white again, a stylish Western skirt and a silk sleeveless blouse.

"So, you were in films?" I asked in a lame attempt to rekindle our conversation at the dinner party. It was like asking such a question of Julia Roberts at a Beverly Wilshire Hotel luncheon in Hollywood.

"Well, I made a lot of silly romantic movies in the 1960s, but they began to bore me."

"Did you make any serious films?" I am abashed now to recall my innocent questions that might have been perceived as condescending ones.

"Of course. *Siddhartha* was one. That film was directed by the American Conrad Rooks and adapted from Hermann Hesse's novel."

I did not bring up that I had learned from my conversation with the elderly journalist that my new friend's appearance in a nude scene in that film caused a sensation in India and that those scenes, according to my source, were cut from the product seen in India. I might add in retrospect that the film became a cult hit worldwide in later years and even had a highly praised restoration in 1996.

After my stop in Bombay, I flew on to the South Indian city of Madras to do a feature on the new beach resorts being developed on the pristine white Indian Ocean sands near the city. As luck would have it, my seat companion was a lone woman posted to the American Consulate in Bombay. She was going to Madras for a weekend wedding of an American friend. The lady from Bombay nicely asked if I wanted to escort her to the wedding, to be held at the Madras Club. At the wedding, an older red-bearded man who escorted the American bride down the aisle was also the American Consul General in Madras. At the reception, he chatted for a bit. I told him I had just been invited to a party that night by an attractive Indian couple. For some mysterious reason, the diplomat leaned over and whispered to me, "Be careful, that couple plays games." He did not elaborate. Their party was a replica of the fun parties in Dacca. Looking back, without doubt the best parties of my life were in South Asia. And if that couple in Madras played games, I say more power to them.

After Madras, I flew up to Calcutta to get to know the city a bit better. I had tea with the American Consul General in his genteel British-style country home in the center of the city. I don't know the history of that house, but it sat in a splendid green oasis in the center of chaos on the ironically named central city street of "Ho Chi Minh Marg." No doubt the Marxist government of the city had a good time changing the colonial name, given the presence of both the American Consulate and the adjoining official residence. The Consul General so nicely said upon my departure, "If there is anything I can do for you in Calcutta, please let me know." I keep wondering to this day what I could have requested.

I also got in touch with my old friend from Delhi University days, Kar. He was now a journalist himself with *The Statesman*, arguably the most consequential newspaper in India. I also rode the trolley that one could board on the Maidan, the city's central park. I rode it all the way to its terminus, then back. That was a cheap way of seeing the city; I have done this also in Bangkok, Hong Kong, and London. I mention that occasion because it was the only time in my life to be pickpocketed. I lost all my cash that day to someone who didn't in fact get much for his efforts. The trolley ride became a feature story. I am sorry I never got to know well the dramatic city of Calcutta, the place of poets and Marxists. Someday that might come to pass, perhaps, should I return to India.

Chapter Eleven

An Unexpected Romance in New Delhi

For the three years I lived in New Delhi, I rented a house, what Americans would recognize as a townhouse, in a fashionable part of the city called Chanaykapuri, or the Diplomatic Enclave. It was a leafy and quiet area not far from the commercial and government center of the city, and, as its name in English suggested, it was the location of most of the city's foreign embassies. The American Embassy was a magnificent compound near the elegant Asoka Hotel, and my house was within walking distance of both places.

Although too expensive for a young journalist, I made financial sacrifices in my monthly budget to afford to live in this upscale neighborhood I had admired from my student days when I occasionally visited the embassy, probably as the crow flies thirty miles from Delhi University. I used to look with longing at the American Club and the tennis courts that were part of the complex, even having a cheeseburger and soft serve ice cream in the dining room on occasion. That's the neighborhood where I lived as a journalist and where I met Rakhi.

Rakhi Seshadri, as alluring a name as was the woman.

I first glimpsed an elderly gentleman walking along Malcha Marg, my residential lane, in the early evening when the temperature cooled somewhat. That was in the autumn of 1978. He routinely took a slow stroll around my crescent and the adjoining one. He was noteworthy because of his formal attire, dark suit, white shirt, and tie. He stood ramrod straight, with a military officer's crop in his hand and folded under his right arm. I thought him a retired army officer, which indeed he was, as I learned later. Once I saw him walking with a younger woman, who moved with an easy grace. Was she his daughter, or perhaps a mistress? No, surely not the latter.

In that winter and early spring of 1979, I saw the two of them frequently. They weren't the only ones walking in the cool evening air, but they were the ones who caught my attention. I admired from a distance that lovely woman at the old man's side and wanted to meet her. One evening, I stepped out as they passed my place and greeted them. They graciously invited me to take the evening air with them.

On a subsequent occasion, I walked with them again. The daughter, Rakhi, was very friendly with a nice gentle manner, a soft voice, and a smile that was heart-stopping. The gentleman, her father as it turned out, was cordial and eventually asked me to join them for tea in their home after the walk. Their home was a stately one at the curve of the crescent on which I lived closer to the main road that ran through the neighborhood. We were joined by the gentleman's wife. The family name was Seshadri. It was a long time before I learned their first names and I never used them in conversation; it was always Mr. and Mrs. Seshadri.

Rakhi came soon to dominate my daydreams. She was perfectly dressed, coiffed, and perfumed, even for an evening stroll, which her father called his constitutional. The mother and father had a nineteenth-century formality about them, although Rakhi was more casual, quick to laugh. To me, she had an allure about which she did not seem aware. A more graceful woman, physically and socially, I had seldom met, and the memory of her then stirs an ache in my heart all these years later.

Rakhi seemed to reciprocate my attraction to her, and occasionally our eyes would meet over chai with her parents. They could see this attraction and seemed a bit amused by it. One evening weeks after we had started walking together more regularly, they invited me to dinner at their home. Rakhi nicely whispered a warning to me that I should wear a coat and tie.

That first dinner at the Seshadri's home is still a vivid memory. Although the table was set with fine china, and we were all formally attired, with candles making the room cozy, we ate with our fingers. I was used to that custom in India from my student days, but I did not expect it in a formal dining room. The vegetarian food was extremely well prepared. Mrs. Seshadri told me she spent a great deal of her time supervising her cook and doing some of the cooking herself. To her, there was nothing more appropriate and civilized than fine food well presented.

Throughout the dinner, of which there would be many subsequently, Rakhi and I exchanged more than an occasional glance as we discussed regional politics and the world scene. Mr. Seshadri was exceptionally well-informed and articulate, as was his wife. I learned that Rakhi was a rising executive at the British bank, Standard Chartered, and had a specialty in foreign exchange. They all inquired pleasantly about my work as a journalist and probed a bit about my family background.

After a month I decided to ask Rakhi to dinner at a nearby restaurant, but because of the family formality, I thought it best to ask her father first for permission.

"It is acceptable, but how are you going to get to the restaurant?" he asked. And then added, "I've not seen you drive a car."

"No, sir, I save money by not having a car, which is not so vital when I spend so much time out of the country."

"Well, then, my driver will take the two of you to your restaurant."

We settled into the back seat of Mr. Seshadri's new black ambassador, an Indian-made vehicle that was most commonly seen on the streets of New Delhi in those days. In the darkened back seat, Rakhi took my hand gently and enclosed her fingers with mine. When you like someone, such a simple gesture can be electric. It helped immensely that Rakhi favored a rose-based perfume, Tea Rose, that surely must be one of the more erotic perfumes ever created by the hand of man.

We had a short ride to the Oberoi Intercontinental Hotel, which had an elegant Chinese restaurant on its top floor. There was a splendid view of the city lights of the commercial area not too far away. Inside it was dim, cozy, and romantic. In those days, it seemed that most fancy restaurants in New Delhi were Chinese, and the food was as good as the décor and the view. Truth is, I hardly noticed what I was eating. My attention was solely on the beautiful woman next to me, a woman in fact I hardly knew. That would change.

"You work at a British bank?" I asked to break the ice.

"Yes, in one of those lighted buildings we can see in the distance," she replied. "I got a job there soon after graduating from the Delhi School of Economics."

"Well, I know that school from years ago when I audited a course in international trade theory. I don't recall too many female students at the school."

"No, not too many then but it was good preparation for a career in international banking. I work on trade and foreign exchange matters. Perhaps someday I can have an assignment in the London head office."

"Don't tell me you went to Miranda House College before the Delhi School?"

"I did."

I was at a loss how to move from the mundane to the more personal things I wanted to know about her. But she helped me along.

"I have not met many single American men. How is it you are not married? You must be about 30?"

"Yes, that is my age. Well, I never met the right woman. How about you?"

"I am 29. I did like a fellow some years ago, but my parents did not approve of him. They still intend to arrange a proper marriage for me, although in truth I am getting too old for a good arranged marriage, or maybe any marriage, for that matter. I don't know what will happen …" Her voice trailed off from what was clearly an uncomfortable topic.

We sat silently for a time, looking out the window. I didn't know what to say. Rakhi was someone I wanted to get to know well, and nothing should happen on this first date to harm our budding relationship.

She broke the silence.

"I feel completely comfortable with you and want to know all about you."

In response, I related briefly my life story of growing up in the Midwest in America and wanting to see the world. India had always attracted me, and now I was here. "Getting married was not a priority, or even an interest in the past …"

We settled into a nice conversation that I hardly recall now because I was looking intently into her eyes, not too focused on chitchat. I do remember that she wore a pink silk sari with a sleeveless blouse. The sheer fabric thrown over her shoulder heightened her sensuality.

"I wish the evening would never end," she said suddenly.

She gently touched my hand, an intimate gesture conveying her desire to know me better. I returned the gesture, putting as much passion as one could into the touching of hands.

We rode back to her home in silence, both feeling that this had been an important night in our lives. I saw her to her door, and then walked over to my nearby flat. I couldn't sleep.

Chapter Twelve

Love in the Heat of Delhi

In the spring and hot summer months of 1979 I had to concentrate on events in Pakistan, and I made several short trips to nearby Lahore. My mind stayed focused on Rakhi in Delhi, however, and I couldn't stand being away from her.

We occasionally went out to dinner, seeking ever more obscure restaurants where we could get a table in a quiet corner for our heart-felt conversations. They continued on long walks around the neighborhood until it got too hot to venture out. It was not simple to pursue a serious romance in the blistering heat of an Indian summer when I could not invite Rakhi into my air-conditioned home, so close to that of her parents, and I did not have a car to drive even to a shady park. A rattletrap taxi from the permanent stand manned by Sikhs in the neighborhood helped a bit on the transport side, but the heat and dust of the oppressive week-end days did its best to temper our growing passion. No, not true at all: the heat did nothing to affect our relationship, which was growing closer by the day, but it did make life physically uncomfortable.

As if understanding my plight without a vehicle, Mr. Seshadri noted one day, "Sir, a proper gentleman has a vehicle at his disposal. I know someone who can fix you up with a second-hand ambassador."

I took him up on the offer and soon had a ten-year-old black ambassador exactly like the old man's, except that it wasn't shiny and had more than a few dents. Though of course not air-conditioned, having that car gave Rakhi and me a wonderful sense of freedom. We could visit a few nearby historical sites and even venture a picnic in a park, if only for a short time before the beggar women and children found us.

There was also the occasional dinner at the Seshadri home. The rigid formality prevailed. One evening, apparently not being able to stand my lack of cultural knowledge drove Mrs. Seshadri to note, "Sir, in our culture, one should not mix bread and rice together on one's plate. The bread comes first, and the rice later."

That remonstrance did little to make me feel more at home there. Nor did Mrs. Seshadri's warning that I should never step an inch into her puja room near the entrance to the dining room. It was a small closet with a statue of a Hindu deity and a pervading smell of incense. Rakhi told me her mother prayed in that closet with the greatest of devotion. She felt she had not done her duty properly in her previous lives and was being punished for having a son, her firstborn, die shortly after his birth. (That event explained her daughter's name; "Rakhi" meant a special relationship with a brother, as well as being one who helped others.)

I tried to get to know Mr. Seshadri a bit better.

"I was in the army pre-partition; in fact, I was in the cavalry and served most of my time in the Punjab."

Going on, he related, "Once I had a hand in putting down a near-riot in Arnarkali Bazaar. That was 1937."

I had to ask where that was. He looked at me as though I were a child. "In Lahore, of course. What is now Pakistan."

"In 1937, did you imagine that India would be partitioned?"

"Of course not. No one could imagine a solution to the communal troubles between Muslims and Hindus. But two separate countries created by a sudden departure of the British from the subcontinent? Never."

"We all hoped that Jinnah would come to his senses and stop his demands for a separate arrangement for the Muslims." Clearly, Mr. Seshadri was reflecting his Hindu perspective.

This exchange and others gave me a glimpse into Mr. Seshadri's life and helped explain his rigid sense in his elderly years of right and wrong. He was Indian army through and through.

If the Seshadri household was cold and formal, Rakhi was warm and loving, soft and yielding, sensuous and provocative.

"I want to make love to you," Rakhi said one day with no pretext.

With great trepidation, we sneaked into my place. I will always remember that she was wearing a dark green silk sari. She was one who could put a lifetime of longing into a never-ending kiss. I discovered that she was as soft as I had long imagined. Our intimacy was heaven-sent. We started thinking how we could be together forever.

We were greatly different after that day. Nothing mattered but being together. I composed a few poems for Rakhi:

> *We're just two people you'd meet*
> *On any ordinary street.*
> *But between us is a feeling*
> *That is very appealing.*

And then another:

> *Stay a moment longer, my dear,*
> *Take my hand and snuggle near,*
> *And tell me stories of your past*
> *To make the evening last.*

Sadly, as the tenderness deepened between Rakhi and me, the formality from her parents turned to coldness.

One evening the old man asked me, "What are your career prospects, actually?"

"Well, the newspaper posted me to Delhi because I had some academic background in South Asia. But I won't be here that long—maybe a year or two more."

"Then what?"

"Another foreign posting. Maybe in Africa, an area I know something about."

"Well, sir," he concluded, "a career wandering the world watching events unfold in one country or another hardly seems satisfactory. What are your academic qualifications?"

"I have a master's degree in international relations."

Maybe he was anticipating my developing serious relationship with his daughter because he replied, "Rakhi has a solid academic background in international economics and is poised to accomplish a great deal in her career."

Why he had to make it personal to Rakhi I didn't want to think about, but there was a sense of foreboding about his remark.

Chapter Thirteen

A Nightmare in Islamabad

Although personally because of Rakhi I did not want to go to Pakistan, a country I otherwise found quite exotic and friendly, I had to go. Baxter wanted me to develop political contacts in Lahore and make a contact or two also at the Foreign Office in Islamabad. It was the third week in November 1979. In those days, there was a PIA flight from Delhi to Lahore, where one had to change planes to Islamabad. The political officer Steve at the American Consulate in Lahore was the same fellow who had been the political officer in Dacca. Steve had extended an invitation to all of us correspondents in Delhi that if we stopped by his house when in Lahore, he would provide a breakfast of scrambled eggs, bacon, and pancakes, as well as good conversation. Who could resist that? Plus he was unusually candid about sharing his political perspective, and even suggesting useful political figures we might look up. I believe all six of my Delhi colleagues from various publications took him up on his offer in the three years he was in Lahore.

I stopped by Steve's comfortable home in Lahore, and sure enough, the two of us had a fine breakfast and a lengthy conversation about political events in Lahore. Pakistani President Zia-ul Haque, the former Army Chief, had led a military coup to depose the elected Zulfiqar Ali Bhutto, who had been put on trial for conspiring in the attempted murder of a political rival in Lahore. A court not surprisingly convicted Bhutto, who was hanged in February 1979 in the chilly predawn hours with no public announcement beforehand. There had been violent demonstrations in Lahore, but Bhutto was gone, and Zia was firmly in command, thanks to the loyalty of the army. The political question was who or what would fill the political gap left by Bhutto's demise. Army control and suppression of political activity could not endure. It was the duty of the foreign press and the diplomatic observers to figure out and report what might come next.

True to his word, Steve suggested a couple of local political figures I might look up when I came back through Lahore, and I made a mental note to do so. It was good that I did. In the meantime, I caught a flight to Islamabad. I planned to be in Islamabad over the upcoming Thanksgiving holiday.

On a Wednesday, the day before Thanksgiving, I had an appointment to chat with David, the young political officer at the U.S. Embassy in Islamabad. After our chat in his office, David and I stopped in the embassy cafeteria for a sandwich. We had hardly been seated when a muffled roar came through the walls of the building, and a few bricks landed in the courtyard just beyond the cafeteria window. Almost instantly, an embassy employee shouted from the cafeteria entrance for all of us to exit the room and move upstairs, ignoring the security barrier. We learned an angry crowd had gathered in front of the building, and we were being evacuated upstairs for our safety. We heard a few muffled gunshots from the embassy's gate. Armed Marine guards shoved past us on their way to the lobby. The last sight I had before heading up the stairs was the gate giving way to the power of a mob.

There were perhaps a hundred of us, embassy employees, both American and Pakistani, as well as assorted visitors, being herded fast up to the third floor. We were all going into the embassy's vault, a secure and ordinarily a highly classified area, for safe haven. There was a deafening cacophony sounding through the halls of the embassy, presumably from rocks, bricks, and even decorative clay flowerpots being thrown against the brick walls. Evidently the mob was inside the compound. From what glimpse I had had of the compound's gate giving way against the mob, they were certainly going to be inside the building soon.

"Everyone move in fast!" ordered the heavily armed marine at the vault entrance. We crowded in.

"Wait!" yelled a voice.

Two marines were carrying a wounded and severely bleeding comrade, another marine. We made way for the three to get into the vault. The wounded one was bleeding from the head and was unconscious; he was moved to a separate smaller room in the vault and was attended to, as best she could, by the embassy health unit nurse. We later learned he had been shot by demonstrators who had breached the embassy doors.

An embassy employee had a shotgun pointed up at the escape hatch. We could hear pounding steps above us on the embassy's roof and we expected the hatch to be opened. Instead, gunshots rang through the metal air filters on the roof near the hatch. Bullets clattered in the air vents but no bullets harmed us.

"Get that vault door closed!" an older embassy employee ordered. It swung shut. As it did, I could see that it was so heavy that nothing short of a serious bomb could dislodge it. We all learned soon enough that once inside the vault, we had no idea what was going on around us, and sounds were heavily muffled, except for resounding pounding around the escape hatch above our heads.

In an adjoining room a senior member of the embassy staff was on a radio with someone. Because it was noontime, there were a number of embassy staff, including the Ambassador, who were not in the embassy when we rushed into the vault. Some of those away from the embassy were on the radio. As I pieced it together, there were thousands of angry demonstrators around the embassy, some with weapons. Why they had attacked the mission was not then apparent. No police were in the area. Observers from afar could see demonstrators on the roof.

Soon we were told smoke was rising from the building. It appeared it had been set afire. At first we in the vault could not tell if a fire had been set. We were sealed off. Still no police presence around the embassy could be seen by outside observers.

Soon we were told the building was fiercely ablaze, and demonstrators had cleared off the rooftop. When we learned this, a marine tried carefully to lift the escape hatch but discovered it would not budge. Harder attempts to open it were not successful either. We surmised it had been wired shut. We were trapped inside a burning building.

Meantime, I heard that senior embassy officials outside the building were in touch with government and army officials to come to our rescue. The U.S. Embassy was but one of dozens in the area, all close to the seat of federal government power. We knew there also was a sprawling army base within 20 miles in the neighboring city of Rawalpindi. Surely security forces were coming.

The mood among the dozens and dozens of individuals in the vault was remarkably calm. For the moment, there was nothing to be done but wait for the next shoe to drop. I had a journalist colleague from Delhi also in the vault. She was from *Time* magazine. Remarkably, she was quickly penciling notes on a pad she had found in one of the vault desks. I started to do the same with a yellow legal pad I found. Quite a story to report. It never entered our minds, or at least not to my knowledge, that we would perish in the vault.

Several hours passed. Outside observers reported that the ranks of the demonstrators, initially estimated to be 10 to 15 thousand, were beginning to thin. The building continued to blaze.

Inside, we could smell smoke, but in the early hours it wasn't too obnoxious. The air was getting stuffy, though, because the vault had not been designed to be sealed with so many individuals for such an extended period. The injured marine died. I learned later his name was Steve Crowley, the youngest at 20 of the contingent at the embassy.

More hours passed. The episode had begun about 12:30 P.M. By 5:00 P.M. the atmosphere in the vault was getting quite smoky, and the floor was decidedly hot. Some floor tiles were curling. An edge of carpeting was smoldering. We held wet paper towels over our faces. There were no forces coming to rescue us. We agreed with our radio contacts outside the building that we had to take action or die in that vault. We were told there were no demonstrators on the roof, and none even around the building. Two marine guards slowly open a back door to the vault. The hallway outside the vault door was a burned-out shell, smoking and hot. The two marines rushed down the smoky corridor and up the stairs to the exit doors to the roof. They opened. The marines raced across the roof to the escape hatch, which had been wired shut. They cut the wires and opened the hatch. Immediately those below began to climb out. First to exit were the Pakistani women on the embassy staff, then the American women, then the Pakistani male staff, and finally the American male staff.

Once on the main roof, we made our way to a lower roof over the destroyed embassy auditorium, from where we could drop ten feet to the ground. The marine in charge, using a fireman's carry, hoisted out Steve Crowley's body. Some staff cried when they saw the marine's heroic action. In the gathering gloom of the late-November evening, no one could be seen around the building. The air outside was distinctly cool. There was still some smoke in the air from the smoldering building, and some lingering tear gas.

As the first survivors of the vault began to move away from the building, a contingent of Pakistani army troops arrived. I believe someone from our group shook hands with the officer in charge. Army trucks arrived. Private cars of family members arrived. There was confusion over who was going where, but most individuals made their way to their nearby homes. Some vault survivors had lived on the embassy compound, but all structures were burned out. I am not certain how all people dispersed.

I walked to a nearby hotel and got a room with another single guy whose name I do not remember. The neighborhood was quiet. The army by this time was all around and firmly in control.

Chapter Fourteen

"We Saved Ourselves in Islamabad" and the Attack in Lahore

How to explain this apparently spontaneous and violent outburst against symbols of American power overseas? It wasn't just the American Embassy in Islamabad that was attacked. So were each of the three American Consulates in Pakistan, as well as the American Express Bank in Lahore, and the American International School in Islamabad. What's more, American offices from Morocco to Indonesia also sustained attacks. We learned that the ostensible catalyst was a seizure the day before in Mecca of the Masjid al-Haram, an Islamic holy site. A Saudi extremist group had taken the action, demanding an end to Saudi oil export to the U.S., among other matters. But the rumor spread like wildfire that the U.S. had perpetrated the attack, or that the Israelis at U.S. behest had done so. No one in those early hours knew the whole story, or what was fact from fiction.

The uprising was a shock, and I put in my draft to Baxter in Delhi that it seemed reminiscent of the sepoy uprising in India in 1857, when the common soldiers rose to massacre the British occupiers of India. Baxter took that flourish out before sending the report on to New York. In Islamabad in November 1979, four individuals lost their lives in the fire: Marine Steven Crowley; U.S. Army Warrant Officer Bryan Ellis; and two Pakistani local employees of the embassy. I could not get the latter two names, to my chagrin. I heard that one demonstrator also had been killed.

What we did know is that in Islamabad, we as hostages in the embassy had saved ourselves. It had not been the Pakistan Army, as

Washington was quick to state. My *Time* magazine colleague, much senior to me, filed her story to that effect, and I understand she was called by her editors to explain why her story differed so fundamentally from the official U.S. explanation. She said she had been in the vault and on the embassy grounds when we hostages had shaken hands with arriving troops at nightfall after all action had died down. She said she knew the truth. Furthermore, I heard it said she threatened to resign and publicly tell her story if her accurate version was not published. It was. The next cover of *Time* had the burning embassy on its cover with the accurate story.

The State Department commandeered the Pan Am round the world daily flight of one of its 747s, which was in Delhi at the time, and chartered it to come empty to Islamabad so that American families and so-called non-essential official personnel could be evacuated. Local PIA flights also chartered quietly brought American dependents from Peshawar, Lahore, and Karachi, and the bursting Pan Am flight left Islamabad as soon as possible bound for Washington, D.C. Just a skeleton staff of officers at the embassy and consulates was left behind.

As for me, I filed my stories and headed for Lahore en route to Delhi. I stopped at the consulate, where I found Steve, the political officer, writing his official account of the troubles. He related what had happened the day before.

In fact, Steve was a bit in shock because he and the three others left at the consulate had had to endure the attack and then organize a sudden ordered departure on only a few hours' notice of non-essential American personnel. As Steve related, who was "official"? Were American teachers at the Lahore American School "official"? No, they decided. Were the U.S.-funded researchers at the infectious disease laboratory "official"? Yes, they decided because they were paid directly with U.S. funds in their contracts. Hastily, with only one suitcase per person, all families gathered the night after the attack and were transported in Pakistani army trucks to a back entrance of the airport. A small 35-seat PIA chartered flight appeared out of the dark, landed and taxied to a reception area out in the runway area far away from the terminal, and with propellers still swirling, all personnel were hastened on the flight without a name check and certainly without tickets. Then the plane turned around, and roared away in the dark, leaving four consulate members stranded. They went to Steve's house, where a large Thanksgiving dinner remained, having been prepared for a reception for Americans that day.

Steve could not take too long to recount other events, but he added that on the day of the attack, now two days previous, he had returned to the office from his home around the corner and discovered to his astonishment that hundreds of police had ringed the consulate. No more had he gotten to his desk then a call came from the German manager of the American Express Bank closer to the congested area of the city that a large mob, maybe in the thousands, had formed out of nowhere and had burned the USIS office nearby and had attacked his bank. The manager, Peter, warned Steve the mob was marching up the Mall Road to burn out the consulate, about thirty minutes away by foot.

In retrospect, Steve could not fully explain why the consulate had not been abandoned in light of the advance notice. Local employees were told to leave. The Americans thought it was their duty to stay with the ship.

The mob descended on the building. The horrendous racket of rocks and bricks rocked the heavy concrete walls. Explosions came from the rear of the office. Later it was discovered that burning consulate vehicles caused the explosions as gas tanks went up.

Steve warned his wife Jane to stay inside. She said the loyal cook had taken down the nameplate on the gate, and the flag. Demonstrators were in the residential area but did not know the house, and the adjoining house of the Consul General, were American properties. Jane had an eighteen-month-old toddler son with her and was seven months' pregnant. During the call Jane related that the Pakistani wife of her pediatrician had pulled up to say, "Get in the backseat under these shawls! You aren't safe here!" Mrs. Anwar was able to drive through the occasional group of demonstrators without notice and got Jane and her young son John to the home of a local industrialist, Naseem Saigol.

Steve credited the police with keeping the demonstrators at bay. The consulate local employees, milling in the crowd, later reported that the ringleaders were not Pakistanis. They were either Iranian or Arab of some undetermined nationality, judging by the mixture of languages heard. Both groups were represented at the nearby Punjab University.

Steve had to get back to his official report, and I had a flight to catch to Delhi.

Rakhi met me at the Delhi airport in her father's car. Ignoring local custom not to demonstrate romantic emotion in public, she threw her arms around me and cried, "Thank God you have returned safely!"

Chapter Fifteen

New Year's in Mianwali District

Desperately, I wanted to spend New Year's Eve with Rakhi in New Delhi. She said there would be many parties to attend, or we could figure out ways to be alone. But old Baxter, true to form, wanted me back in Pakistan, which now had world attention. Instead of cuddling with my new love, I headed back to Lahore. What developed became one of the special memories of my life.

I took an early morning flight to Lahore on December 26, the day after Christmas. I took a taxi directly from the airport to the nearby home of Malik Wazir Ali, a retired Civil Service of Pakistan official and now the General Secretary of Air Vice Marshal Asghar Khan's political party, the Tehreek e Istaklal (the Movement for Independence). As Wazir Ali had explained to me in several previous conversations, inspired because Steve had suggested I meet him, the Tehreek stood for parliamentary democracy, free and fair elections, and the rule of law. My desire to see Wazir Ali wasn't so much to learn more about the Tehreek as it was to hear Wazir Ali's perspective on the current Pakistani political scene. But truthfully, I wanted to have chai with him just because I liked who he was, a real gentleman with a keen sense of humor and, I sensed, great innate decency.

We had tea in the front garden of his old house near the cantonment, the colonial-era name for a military base. It was chilly and sunny, I recall vividly. We had a relaxed exchange and then, surprisingly, Wazir Ali's wife and grown daughter drove up in their old VW Beatle. I had had no occasion to meet them on previous visits to Wazir Ali's home.

They greeted me with such a friendly manner that I liked them instantly. Wazir Ali's wife, whom I got to know subsequently as Nasra, reported that they were imminently leaving town for a week to inspect lands they owned in distant western Mianwali District. I had been there six months before. It was a wild area of sturdy farmers and tall warriors aligned to various local warlords along the Northwest Frontier Province, an untamed tribal area bordering Afghanistan.

With hardly a moment's hesitation, Wazir Ali said, "Scott, why don't you come with us?" The ladies enthusiastically echoed the invitation. I jumped at the chance. I was lonesome, and here were clearly nice people inviting me to travel to a colorful area of the country. I agreed, and within the hour we were all off on a week's adventure.

We were comfortable enough in the family's old green Mazda. I sat up front with Wazir Ali, who drove. He said, call me Wazir, and it is Nasra and daughter Shahnaz. And I was Scott. So began a week's trip of pure pleasure that was not likely to involve being shot at or suffocated by fire and smoke. It was enough that I was with people who were so welcoming, and who, I discovered soon enough, also fun-loving, always seeing humor in any encounter. In fact, I did see a slice of important political and social life in the countryside, so the feature I ultimately wrote for Baxter and our stateside newspaper justified my time on the road.

We drove first to a large town, Faisalabad, about 75 miles south of Lahore. It was dark before we arrived at the home in town of a friend of the Wazir Ali's. I had been to Faisalabad six months earlier during a swing through the countryside of the Punjab province. Faisalabad was a substantial town with many small commercial establishments, maybe a tannery, and probably a couple of factories producing cotton fabric. Cotton was the main cash crop. But I did not see any of this on that night-time stop.

In the morning, still cool and sunny, the three of us took off on the two-lane country road from Faisalabad to Bhakkar, a small town in Mianwali District. If Bhakkar was our destination, it didn't seem too important to the family. Instead, Wazir and Nasra saw to it that I understood the landscape we were traversing, a landscape that became more rugged and arid the farther west toward Afghanistan we ventured.

Every ten miles or so, Wazir would stop so that we could tramp into a field to visit a locally famous religious shrine. The countryside was dotted with them. They were hundreds of years old. I think some pre-dated the arrival of Islam a thousand years previous. How many Westerners travel to Bhakkar? A precious few; and of those, who had a guide to point out the shrines and other historical spots? It was a once-in-a-lifetime opportunity. I learned after that week from Wazir and Nasra that it is the journey that counts more than the destination. If that is a cliché, so be it. I lived it. Our destination was rather colorful, too, as it developed.

In the late afternoon we arrived in Bhakkar, a small dusty town whose purpose was to serve the basic consumer needs of the farmers in the area. What I learned is that all the farmers owed their livelihoods to a local landlord, or zamindar, who owned the land on which they tilled. Zamindar in the Pakistan context is a term for a major landowner and feudal ruler who took care of his tenants, who lived on the great family's land generation after generation. Our host, Captain Ahmed Nawaz, was the local chief of this area. As zamindars went in the rural areas of Pakistan, Ahmed Nawaz probably was a smaller operator. I failed to learn enough of his history and that of his family. But I observed a lot about his relationship with his people. I was told he had a family home in the countryside, but we were his guests at his town residence. The house was a bare-bones structure with minimal furniture and no fireplaces that I recall. There was only cold water available, and the temperature was chilly day and night. There was lots of personal warmth, though, because Ahmed Nawaz was a courtly gentleman who treated me like an honored guest. Clearly, he held Wazir Ali in high esteem also. I got a cot in a spare room, with an attached bathroom with a Western-style toilet with no seat.

We were served greasy roasted chicken for dinner. It was good. We had roasted chicken at every meal for the next five days. There was no woman around, no Mrs. Captain. There was roasted chicken, though.

The next morning, the 28th, and frosty as always, Wazir and I spent hours sitting with Ahmed Nawaz in the small front garden of his house. He had a big wooden chair in the mostly dirt yard, and a smaller one next to him. There was a telephone on a little table near his chair. The phone had a long cord snaking into the house. He often picked up the receiver to be connected to someone in the local telephone office because one could not dial from the ancient instrument. Whoever was on the other end, an operator obviously, always answered immediately when Nawaz picked up the receiver.

We watched as a barber came to shave the great man in the yard. We all had tea, even the barber had a cup at some distance removed. We could tell there were many men—no women—lined up at the nearby gate to his compound. Wazir told me they were Ahmed's tenants seeking help from the old man, who apparently held court from time to time when he was in town.

A guard, called a choukidar, let one man at a time enter the compound. Each admitted visitor followed the same procedure. He would approach the chair, bend down and touch the Captain's feet, and then clasp his hands to form a gesture of prayer while murmuring, "*As-salamu-alaykum*," Arabic for "peace be upon you." The Captain would gesture for the man to sit and explain what his problem was. The farmer would tell a short story, and then the Captain would invariably pick up the phone, give an order, and then reassure the man all would be well. The tenant would bow and depart, and in a minute another farmer would be admitted for the same procedure, which stretched through the whole morning. I forgot: Often the Captain would send the tenant off with a little cup of tea, and he would sometimes ask if the man needed something to eat. Most declined the offer of food.

Wazir told me later that most of the requests were very personal; one man said his wife had run away with someone else, and the request was for her to be tracked down and returned. Another man said a neighbor had stolen something. After hearing each request, the Captain asked the telephone operator to get him the local police chief (called an SP for Superintendent of Police). Or, the request might have been to the local DC (Deputy Commissioner). Both of these officials were federal government officials with considerable authority and latitude to do their jobs, but I saw they also took orders from Captain Ahmed Nawaz. Was it this way throughout the countryside? No doubt it was so.

That evening I wanted, foolishly, to take a walk around the town. It was confining to be in the compound. Nawaz first said it was too dangerous, but he reconsidered and had one of his men follow me at ten feet. Shahnaz joined me. We wandered into the nearby bazaar, brightly lit with glaring, unshielded fluorescent bulbs above the various stalls selling foodstuffs such as fried potatoes in a crusty pastry. Nothing untoward happened. I don't think the local men paid us any heed, but that surely was because they recognized one of Ahmed Nawaz's men shadowing us.

Chapter Sixteen

The Soviet Invasion of Afghanistan

The next morning, December 29, was particularly chilly. As was his custom, Wazir had arisen before dawn so that he could listen to the BBC early-morning international news broadcast. I joined him in the garden, sleepy and needing of a cup of chai. Wazir looked at me with a twinkle in his eye, and asked, "Scott, what would you say if I told you, hypothetically, that last night the Soviets launched an invasion of Afghanistan?" I muttered something to the effect that that would be rather unlikely and went back to sipping my tea.

Wazir probed and added, "Well, let's just pretend that the Soviets did invade. What would you predict would be the American response?"

Again, I dismissed the hypothetical question as so much fantasy. But I probably speculated that the U.S. response would be limited to rhetorical condemnation.

He persisted, "What if the U.S. pledged millions in military aid to Pakistan?"

I recall thinking this game must have a serious purpose. I asked what he was getting at.

"These two events have happened while we slept. The Soviets have invaded Afghanistan, and the U.S. has pledged to send massive military assistance to Pakistan to protect the country."

"What? Why would all this happen?"

Wazir speculated that the Soviets were reviving the Great Game of the latter nineteenth century when Russia contested with the British for control of Afghanistan. The Russians had ultimately been repulsed by the fearsome Afghan warriors, with assistance from the British army.

Wazir suggested the Soviet goal now was two-fold: to put down a growing Muslim challenge to their regional authority; and ultimately to seek a warm water port in Karachi. Hence, the immediate U.S. military assistance to protect Pakistan.

I shivered to think that the current military action was hardly a hundred miles west of Bhakkar.

I recalled my previous visit to Bhakkar in the summer of 1979. My political assistant, Ali, as good as was Ahmed in Dacca, had set up a meeting between a local leader and me at a small house in a grove of trees out in a field. (Perhaps that leader had been a relative of Captain Ahmed Nawaz?)

My rented and aged Range Rover pulled up to the house. There were a few other vehicles there. The front door opened, and a handsome, charismatic man of about 35 greeted me in a friendly fashion. He motioned for me to enter the small building. As I crossed the threshold, about 20 tall and heavily armed men stood up in unison. I practically backed out of the structure because I was so surprised and intimidated. The attitude however was friendly. Although I was but a journalist and young, I represented to them America at that moment as if I were the American Ambassador.

We all sat as I conversed with the English-speaking leader. We talked of the growing Soviet threat to the region. He said if the Soviets threatened his lands, they would meet stiff resistance. I eyed the stern-faced men with him, all armed with shotguns. I believed him about the stiff resistance and the firm resolve of his men, although I recall thinking that shotguns would hardly count much against Soviet soldiers with automatic weapons.

That meeting six months earlier now haunted me. The area in which we sat with tea might be a battleground in the next year. Fortunately for Pakistan, that never came to pass. History records that the U.S. did provide military assistance and helped the Pakistan Army, a force in itself to be reckoned with, to arm Afghan resistance fighters who took the battle into Afghanistan in the years to come. Ultimately, as the world knows, they pushed the Soviets out.

Chapter Seventeen

A Pakistani Village and What Women Wanted

The next day all three of us drove to a nearby village. Although I assume now that that was where Wazir Ali had his land, I cannot recall now the reason for the village visit. The experience there that morning, however, remains vivid. As soon as the village women saw the two educated Pakistani women, that is Nasra and Shahnaz, climb from the green Mazda, the village women swarmed around them, speaking earnestly, pleading almost, for the ladies to hear their stories. They ignored Wazir and me. We waited a long time before Nasra and Shahnaz could rejoin us.

"What was that all about?" asked Wazir.

Shahnaz answered, "They asked us about birth control. They said their husbands want as many children as possible, but the wives do not but cannot stop getting pregnant."

Shahnaz went on, "They know there are methods of birth control, but they said their husbands do not cooperate. They asked us what they should do, and could they use some form of contraception that the husbands would not know about."

Wazir asked, "What did you advise?"

I wish I could report what Shahnaz and Nasra advised the women to do. But village women crowded around us and the question went unanswered. The image of the women desperately imploring Shahnaz and Nasra as educated, urbane women to give them the answers has stayed with me all these decades. Up to that point, I had assumed the village men and women together wanted as many children as they could as a form of insurance, to have children to take care of them in later years. I glimpsed that day that my simple assumption was not entirely correct.

In the afternoon, the three of us walked along a canal lined with trees. For those who have not travelled in rural Punjab, it may come as a surprise that the countryside is lined with a fair number of substantial canals that channel the waters from the Indus River and other smaller rivers from the Himalayas through Pakistan to the sea far south. The British built most of these irrigation canals, but I believe in the 30 years since Pakistani independence, more canals had been dug. What also comes as a surprise to first-time visitors is how attractive the canals are. They usually have earthen berms on both sides, and nice shade trees growing on those raised mounds of earth. The canals provide a pleasant place to stroll, even though they were far into the hinterlands.

I recall also the conversation I had with Wazir. He had been a member of the Civil Service of Pakistan, the highly competitive and prestigious bureaucratic service that ran the country, and he had had a senior diplomatic posting in Washington in the late 1950s and into the Kennedy Administration. That must have been a plum assignment. Later still, he had been appointed a director at the Asian Development Bank in Manila. In short, his career had been one of accomplishment and distinction. Now, he was retired from government service and was devoting himself to political work. I recall we discussed what I might do when I retired from journalism. He suggested political work. That avenue had not occurred to me, just as retirement was too far off to be given too much thought. I haven't followed Wazir's advice yet, but if I may have a few years left, I might still dip my toe in political waters, not as a candidate but as a worker.

A word must be said of Nasra. To me, she seemed a woman of few words, almost a woman of mystery. She took a lively interest in conversations, but she did not quickly express herself, at least not too often in my limited experience, but she always had a slightly amused look on her face, as if she understood things the rest of us could not grasp. At the time of our Bhakkar trip, I did not know that she already had a long career behind her as an educator in Karachi, where since 1949 she had worked to establish schools for young girls from the poorest of neighborhoods. Those schools, collectively known as the Nasra Trust Schools, continued to function even though she was living in Lahore. Nasra was in Lahore, I learned much later, to support her husband's political efforts. As I recall Nasra in those days, the words "nice" and "loving" spring immediately to mind.

To complete the picture at that time of this extraordinarily gracious family was Shahnaz, a fourth-grade teacher at the Lahore American School. She was cheerful, quick to laugh, and a bit of a tease, just as her father was when he played a game with me about the BBC news regarding the Soviets and Americans. I can imagine Shahnaz doing something like that in a good-natured way. Little could any of us know that Shahnaz in the decades to come would rise to amazing heights of accomplishment, first in politics to become a member of the national assembly and then to be the Prime Minister's special assistant and finally, State Minister of Education. After that she made a name for herself developing a national philanthropic organization, and finally, much later in life, she became president of a private university in Karachi.

I wish to relate these stories to explain that I had become acquainted, purely by accident, with a family of great distinction. And to top it off, all three were presented the Sitar-e-Imtiaz award, one of Pakistan's highest civilian honors. All of these achievements I am reporting in this document came later in life (except for Wazir, who had already been awarded the distinction), but at the time all I knew was that I was lucky enough to be travelling with such a genteel family, the likes of which few people ever encounter.

Chapter Eighteen

Journey Back to Lahore

Starting on December 31, we began our journey back to Lahore, breaking it into two days. We spent New Year's Eve in a small town whose name I do not remember. Wazir met with a roomful of local leaders, and I sat impassively with them, not understanding more than occasional words. My study of Hindi years earlier in Delhi should have helped a bit because Urdu is not that different from Hindi in its spoken form, but truth is, I didn't have a clue what was said. That night, Wazir and I shared a small bed. Not a dramatic New Year's Eve, but a satisfying one to be with people I admired.

On January 1, we stopped in Chiniot, a small town known for its craftsmen who could fashion the most intricately carved wooden objects, including furniture. Nasra and I admired medium-sized mirror frames. I bought one, and she considered purchasing a similar frame but finally decided it was too extravagant. I don't think she noticed that in the end, I purchased two of the frames. Sometime later, I gave her the second carved frame as a gift to say thank you for including me on the Bhakkar trip. She was touched, and I think now that never have I given a gift as appreciated as was that mirror frame. I still have my frame with reflective glass I had fitted later in New Delhi. I know that, these many decades later, Nasra's mirror is still in her family.

I got to Lahore and immediately caught a plane back to Delhi, anxious to see Rakhi and try to explain what an unusual week I had had. There were reports also to write. Old Baxter seemed to be coming around to a grudging acknowledgement that I had a contribution to make in journalism.

Chapter Nineteen

Interlude in Kashmir

The next few months I managed to stay close to Delhi to be with Rakhi. I justified myself professionally by doing several feature reports, including one on the four existing vestiges of the former glory of the Mughal Empire. The court had been first in Lahore, then south of Delhi in the desert (Fatipur Sikri), then in Agra where also is the Taj Mahal, and then finally in Delhi itself. The palaces and mosques are well-preserved, and it was not hard to recreate for readers what it must have been like to have lived when that part of the world was controlled by the Muslims.

The romantic relationship with Rakhi became much more intense, but also more strained. One cannot have a romantic relationship that remains static; it either grows and with good luck transitions into an engagement and a marriage, or it falls apart. Ours had been developing cracks. I was an itinerant journalist; she was a serious rising banking executive.

Mr. Seshadri one night put it bluntly, "What kind of future can you offer our daughter? One journalistic posting after another? How can Rakhi pursue her career?"

What he did not say, I suspect, is that he did not approve of journalism as a serious career. After all, what did a reporter do? Just observe and write stories. Seshadri did not subscribe to the lofty definition of journalism as producing the first draft of history.

Left unspoken but an important factor was that I was foreign and a Christian, whereas the Seshadri family was high-caste Hindu Brahmin. How could members of these two religions coexist? Mr. and Mrs. Seshadri, I must state, were good and decent people, but they came from a far different culture from mine.

Rakhi was highly educated and more liberal than her parents were, but she too had not travelled abroad. (I should note that Mrs. Seshadri in her youth had been an assistant to a maharaja's wife and had travelled in luxury to London, Paris, and Milan. She had been worldly in her youth, but in her mature years she had become a highly conservative and cautious individual.) While the cultural differences between Rakhi and me hardly seemed to exist in our romantic days in New Delhi, we were living a completely artificial existence in that cosmopolitan city.

Into the growing tension of what direction our relationship should take, we came up with a foolish idea to spend a long weekend together in Kashmir. New Delhi in May is excruciatingly hot, with a sky brown from the dust of the Ganges plain oppressing the landscape. In the days of the Mughul Empire, the emperor and his court would shift in the pre-monsoon heat to the coolness of the Kashmir valley, surrounded as it is by high mountains. We thought it would be good to be alone for a few days, and it certainly would be pleasant to be in cool weather amid mountains and pine forests. Rakhi's parents were horrified with such a trip but powerless to stop their headstrong daughter from exerting her first independence as an adult.

We caught a flight from New Delhi to Srinagar, Kashmir's capital. We rented a houseboat on the lovely lake on the edge of the town. We spent quite a lot of time in that luxury houseboat, decorated like a Mughal palace might have been with lush red pillows, carpets, and hanging silks, and candle-lit lanterns at night. We hired a car and driver to take us for a picnic into the mountains. We took several boat rides around the lake, much as one might do in Venice. We also looked up Shireen, who invited us to tea at her pleasant and spacious home. (Recall I had met her a year earlier in Bombay.) She was gracious, and it was pleasant to see how the well-to-do lived in Kashmir.

If Kashmir was a pleasant experience on the surface, both Rakhi and I knew we should not have defied her parents and taken the trip. It was not pleasant to return to New Delhi. We faced open hostility from her parents, especially soon afterward when I got my onward assignment as a correspondent to Nairobi. Was Rakhi going to come or not? Were we to be married?

Chapter Twenty

A Final Visit to Lahore

In May I made a brief return visit to Lahore. It was my last trip there because my departure from Delhi and the subcontinent was fixed for early June 1980. Once I got through customs in Lahore, I took a taxi to the Wazir Ali household, not far from the airport, as I remembered from my visit there on a chilly December morning five months earlier. To my surprise, the family was living in a new house just behind the old one in whose front garden I had sat with Wazir. The new house still retained that nice new-house smell of fresh concrete and tile. The old house was being used as a newly established school for a few children taught by Nasra.

I was lucky to find everyone at home because I had had no way of arranging a visit on short notice. It was late afternoon, and at teatime it was the custom for people routinely to just show up. Nasra greeted me with an affectionate hug. Forty years on I remember that embrace. In her generation, Pakistani women did not greet foreign men with hugs, I didn't think. Evidently, I was wrong, or I was the exception. Either way, it was wonderful to see her. Wazir gave me a firm handshake with the usual twinkle in his eye as if he was plotting to pull a fast one on me the way he did that December morning in Bhakkar. Shahnaz was home from the Lahore American School. It was a bonus that I got to meet her three children. There were the girls Shombie, about nine years old, and Fatima, probably about 11. They were shy to meet me but that disappeared within minutes. They were so cute. There also was Amir, a tall and good-looking fellow about 13. The two girls were students at the Lahore school. I wonder now whether Shombie was in her mother's class.

We all may have talked a bit about politics, but our conversation was more that which would happen among friends who had not seen each other in some months. That is, exchanging stories and gossip. Shahnaz filled me in, though, on politics vis-à-vis her school.

"The decision of the consulate after the attack that the American teachers were not official Americans caused trouble. They thought they were official."

"In the end, what they did was organize a caravan to drive to the border with India (fifteen miles east of Lahore) and somehow get across so that they could drive on to Delhi. They are back now, but not too happy with the consulate."

They invited me to stay for dinner, which was a cheerful event. When I did depart, it was with a heavy heart because that home was one of good cheer, humor, and mutual affection such as one rarely encounters in life.

The next morning, I went to the consulate to check-in with Steve, the political officer. I found staffing a bit different. The Consul General had been recalled to Washington, leaving Steve in charge. He reported to me that the few Americans in place were frightened that there would be another attack at any moment. The fear was that those who had led the attacks were still in town, and they would take advantage of any excuse to return to burn down the consulate, an action that had been thwarted by the police in November. There never was a repeat attack, fortunately.

Steve laughed that his official duties had expanded. He had been asked to hand out awards at the annual flower show in the city! And, as the consulate head, he had been invited to the Governor's mansion for an extensive dinner in honor of the visiting Chinese premier and Pakistan's president, General Zia-ul Haque. This is what Steve related:

"When it came time to find our seats at the dozens of round tables elegantly set, there were name tags at each seat. I found myself placed next to the Iranian Consulate representative. I'll bet the Pakistani protocol folks had fun with that seating arrangement!"

"Why?"

"Because official instruction had come from Washington that, with the hostage situation going on in Tehran, there could be no socializing—not even hand-shaking—between Iranian and American representatives. Undoubtedly, the Pakistan protocol folks knew this. So why not play a game and see how we handled it."

"What happened?"

"Well, as it turned out, I knew the young Iranian fellow a bit. We were the same age, in fact. He and his wife had been to our home socially before the hostage situation occurred, and his little kids came to our house for play dates with our little one."

"The Iranian looked pained and we stood hesitantly at our chairs for a moment. Then I thought, 'What the hell' and stuck out my hand to shake his. He seemed relieved and took my hand. After that we got seated and chatted about our families and the weather."

Steve added, "Hope Washington doesn't find out."

After my chat with Steve, I met a few other Pakistan contacts in Lahore and then made my way to the airport.

Chapter Twenty-One

Delhi Farewell

The day of my departure from New Delhi drew close. I could see that Rakhi was not coming with me to Nairobi, that much was clear. She was too attached to her parents and needed their approval. She also had a promising career that could not be lightly abandoned.

What was our last full evening together, Rakhi gave me a departure gift, a small metal bracelet that she said was to be worn on my right wrist.

"I want you to have this amulet, which will protect you wherever you go."

"How is that?" I asked, puzzled.

"My name is Rakhi, but the name means more than just a girl's name. It stands also for an amulet of the same name. It is usually meant as a binding token between brother and sister. But I am giving this to you because I no longer have a brother, and I want you to be protected wherever you go. And never, ever take it off, and never forget me."

I muttered a thank you, choked up. We shed tears.

The night before my departure, Rakhi suddenly showed up at my door. I could not believe she was standing there.

"I'm coming with you to Nairobi."

"Will you marry me, then?"

"Yes."

End of Part I

Part II

East Africa

Chapter One

A New Beginning

Previously, Scott had told of his last night in New Delhi, when the love of his life, the stunning Indian woman named Rakhi, had astonished him with a late-night knock on his door. They had parted some hours earlier with the understanding that she could not leave New Delhi with him because of her parents' objections to her marrying a non-Hindu, and the loss of her promising position with a British bank in New Delhi.

After opening the door and finding Rakhi before him, he could not think of anything to say. They had already said a final goodbye earlier in the evening. His momentary loss of words didn't matter.

Rakhi stated, "I'm coming with you to Nairobi."

Scott asked, "You will marry me, then?"

She replied, "Yes."

They stood and looked in each other's eyes for a long moment. The import of their words needed to be grasped. Scott finally extended his arms and enfolded Rakhi in an embrace, one he would never forget. They kissed gently and long. Then they just stood there in the entrance, holding each other, neither moving.

"What do we do now?" Scott asked, overwhelmed.

"You could invite me in for a few moments."

"Oh." He led Rakhi by the hand inside, slowly, and she perched on one of the packed boxes that filled the entrance.

"What changed?" Scott asked.

"I realized that you are the man I want to be with, come what may. You are kind and decent. You offer the promise of an exciting life in a world larger than India, although this will always be my home. And you like India, even if we won't live here."

"Do your parents know your decision?"

"No, we must tell them. What time does your flight to Nairobi leave tomorrow?"

"Two in the afternoon."

"So, come to my parents' home at eight tomorrow morning and have breakfast with us. They will expect you have come around to say goodbye to them. Then I will be off to the Kenyan Embassy to apply for a visa."

Of course, he realized, she did not have a visa to Kenya, nor an airline ticket.

"What if they forbid you to leave the house?"

"They won't."

With another tender kiss and embrace, Rakhi departed to walk the few steps to her parents' nearby home. Scott watched her without closing his door. When he could see she was safely inside the gate to her parents' home, he slowly closed his door and sat down on a box to think of what was about to happen. He didn't sleep that night.

Chapter Two

New Delhi Departure

A few minutes before eight the next morning, Scott rang the buzzer at the Seshadri's gate. The choukidar opened the gate, and Rakhi appeared at the door, looking gamely cheerful but with red eyes.

She showed Scott into the dining room, where her parents were seated and already having some toast and yogurt. Mr. Seshadri rose and shook hands formally. Mrs. Seshadri faintly smiled a greeting. They knew something was up.

Rakhi broke the silence, "I'm going to join Scott in Nairobi as soon as I can get a tourist visa to Kenya," she announced evenly. Her eyes were steady and her tone firm.

Rather than an explosion of protest, Mr. Seshadri in an equally firm and steady voice replied, "Have you thought through the implications?"

"Yes, we are getting married as soon as we can get it arranged, and that will likely be abroad. Probably in the States," was Rakhi's reply.

The Seshadris sat a bit in silence. Rakhi's mother began to cry, but gently and more to herself than for effect. Then she said, "What do you want us to say?" Mr. Seshadri looked evenly at Scott, expecting him, not his daughter, to answer the mother's question.

Scott replied, "We know this is a shock. I will need to depart alone this afternoon for Nairobi, and if Rakhi has a change of heart in the next week or so while awaiting a Kenyan visa, I will understand."

Rakhi's father eyed Scott coldly and replied, "Sir, in this country daughters do not run off wildly to get married. Rakhi's mother and I will discuss this privately. I'm sure you have arrangements to make now for your own departure." With that, he arose, and it was clear Scott should depart, even though he had not eaten a bite. He nodded to the Seshadris and departed with a hand-squeeze from Rakhi, who followed him to the gate.

"I am going to the Kenyan Embassy now, and I will meet you at the airport at noon in the check-in area to say goodbye." Scott nodded and turned.

Rakhi said softly to his back, "I love you." That was a phrase she had not used very often in their experience.

Scott turned and said from five paces, "I love you too."

At noon, Scott arrived at the airport, with only one suitcase and a carry-on bag. His other possessions in packed boxes would be sent as air freight. The departure area was extremely crowded, as it must have been every hour since the facility had been opened many years earlier. No Rakhi in sight. He struggled with the crowd to get his boarding pass and check his bag. Then he stepped back from the throng at the counter to survey the crowd. Rakhi was just making her way to him.

To Scott, she looked forlorn, but determined at the same time. "I made the tourist visa application, and the visa should be ready in a week."

Scott was afraid to embrace her because it was not the custom in India to do so in public. Instead, he touched her arm for a moment, and then said, "I will be waiting on the other end. I am so sorry, especially for your mother. I hope they do not forbid your coming."

"They won't do that. At my age, it is no longer easy to arrange a proper marriage for me, and that they appreciate more than I. Still, by running away, I have created a debt to them that can never be repaid," she added, with perception beyond her years.

"But I want to live!" she interjected. With that, she wrapped her arms around Scott, gave him a firm kiss on his lips, and turned to depart. Her last words were, "Wait for me. I will come."

Chapter Three

Nairobi Reunion

Scott did wait for Rakhi in Nairobi. It took about a week for her to get the tourist visa and the ticket. After those were in her hands and an arrival date set, Scott counted down the hours until her arrival.

In the meantime, Scott checked into his Nairobi office, which was as friendly as the New Delhi office had been cold. His supervisor, Bob, not a lot older than Scott himself at 31, enthusiastically welcomed him, warning him that the political situation in Kenya was not as dramatic as had been the case for Scott in Dacca or Islamabad, and politics was not a sport as was the case in New Delhi. "No embassy burnings at least," he added. "The rest of the region is and likely will continue to be in turmoil." That was an understatement.

On the day after his arrival, Bob invited Scott to lunch at the Muthaiga Club, a classy country club in the far suburbs. Scott wondered why old man Baxter had never taken him to lunch in the three years they were together in New Delhi. Bob explained that work could wait; it was important to get to know each other.

After being seated, Bob asked, "What's your experience in Africa? I recall from your personnel file that you were in the Peace Corps?"

"I was. I lived in Sierra Leone for two years, but that was a decade ago. I taught English, so to speak, in a little school upcountry in a village named Makali."

"Why do you say 'so to speak' that you taught English?"

"Because I'm not sure I was very good, and it is unlikely any lessons I presented stuck with the kids, who were super friendly, by the way. But I learned a lot culturally. I lived in a cinderblock hut on the Paramount

Chief's compound, and that kept me well-protected. Although truthfully, the people were so welcoming that I felt totally safe."

"The one local custom I could not adopt was the eating of fresh monkey brains right out of the skull of a slaughtered animal. The boys in class considered monkey brains a delicacy and kept pestering me to try them. What I did try, though, was palm wine, that is, fermented palm tree sap. All the village men drank it, especially those who sat in the shade and watched the women till the land. I thought the drink was horrible, but other volunteers claimed to like it."

Bob replied, "Good experience culturally to help understand Africa. But this vast continent has great local differences; you are not likely to find the Kenyan people as openly friendly as the West Africans. Although maybe you will be more successful on that score than I have been."

Expounding further, Bob explained that the Muthaiga Club where they now dined would not be where Scott would find, nor ever seek to entertain, any political contacts or leaders.

"The management of the club would not want to offend the government by having any hint of partisan politics at the club. The members here are the movers and shakers in the commercial and social world, and mostly expats at that." He added. A glance around the dining room confirmed Bob's observation. Those dining were sleek and well-dressed and would have fit into any country club setting in the States, although actually Scott did not have much personal experience in that regard.

In the days before Rakhi's arrival, a few of Scott's new acquaintances among the foreign correspondents took him to dinner at Nairobi's newest dining attraction, a spacious restaurant named the Carnivore with outdoor seating and specializing in grilled meat, including wild game. Diners could choose from a menu that included zebra, crocodile, gazelle or almost any other wild animal that could be found. Scott found that, to him, the grilled meat all tasted pretty much the same and was delicious, notably because of the charcoal grilling and spices used in preparation. He considered also that this might be the last meat he would consume now that he was about to greet his love, who was raised in an absolutely strict vegetarian household.

Rakhi's arrival day drew near. Scott could hardly think of anything else but seeing her. On the afternoon of her arrival, which was conveniently a Friday, Scott showed up at the Nairobi airport early. The airport was more modern than the one in New Delhi, and it was not the tourist season, so it was comfortable and not overly crowded. Scott found a seat at the international arrival area and opened a cheap detective novel to pass the hour or two until her plane arrived. He couldn't read more than a sentence, though, until his attention wandered. What was it going to be like, alone with her from now on?

The plane from New Delhi drew up to the arrivals area. Passengers had to deplane onto the tarmac and walk into the arrival building. Scott had to wait, pacing.

There she was, a vision in a sleeveless black silk blouse and white pants, a more Western appearance than she had deemed appropriate in New Delhi. They embraced in the terminal, and then withdrew a pace to look at each other. The scent of Tea Rose, that most exotic of perfumes, was in the air.

"Thank God you are here!" Scott exclaimed.

"Yes, and I'm thrilled about it!"

Scott had been loaned the office car and driver for this special occasion, so it was easy to get into the car and head into town. In the back seat, they held each other's hands tightly.

"Where are you taking me?" Rakhi asked with a twinkle in her eye and an inviting smile on her lips.

"To a place you will never forget." Scott replied. In fact, he did take Rakhi to a luxurious hotel, the Intercontinental, which she never did forget. There was champagne on ice waiting, and several bouquets of colorful flowers. They didn't leave the room until Monday morning, almost three days later. Except for a tense weekend trip to Kashmir a few months earlier, their relationship had been conducted mostly in the presence of others and had been constrained by a conservative culture. Now they had the luxury of privacy, and they were private.

Late Saturday night, after 24 hours getting to know each other in the most intimate ways, Rakhi turned to Scott and asked in a sleepy voice that belied the importance of her thoughts, "Do you love me?"

"Of course, how can you doubt it?"

"No, I mean, why do you love me? We come from very different cultures, and it will take a long time for us to understand each other. I am not very much like you, even if I speak English and studied economics. I am a Hindu, an Indian, and then a woman, in that order."

"Well, put like that, I can't pretend to understand you, yet. But you are a good person, soft, gentle, smart, caring, and who knows in what order those qualities rank. You are exotic, coming from a foreign culture, and that is alluring. I want to learn your culture so I can know you and love you even more."

Scott added other qualities he admired in Rakhi, "You are unpredictable, sensuous, and exciting. For example, you are here, against all logic."

Rakhi's eyes grew red and moist as she thought of her mother, crying when she learned her daughter was running off with a foreign man. They were silent for a while.

Sensing the inevitable question from Scott, "Yes, I love you also," Rakhi finally stated. "You are sensitive, decent, respectable, and more calculating than you may at first appear. I like those qualities. But it is not going to be easy to make this relationship work."

Concluding, Rakhi added, "I need a man who will tell me every day that he loves me."

Sighing because she understood more of life than he, she reached out to him for a long kiss that confirmed again to the innocent Scott that Rakhi was the woman he wanted in life.

Chapter Four

Onward to the States

Rakhi and Scott emerged from the Intercon Hotel on Monday morning, anxious to start real preparations for their new life together. Scott had secured a visa appointment for Rakhi at the U.S. Embassy to apply for a fiancé visa. There were reservations to be made for their travel to the States to get married. Scott was entitled to home leave after his direct transfer from India, and he was impatient to get started and show off a bit of the States to Rakhi, to say nothing about a marriage.

Over the weekend, Rakhi also had told Scott that in New Delhi she had requested merely a leave of absence from Standard Chartered Bank, and that there was a prospect of a position for her in Nairobi, where there was an even larger Standard Chartered branch than in New Delhi. She wanted to introduce herself personally to bank management.

They were so focused on logistical matters that they hardly noticed how much cooler and pleasant it was in Nairobi than it had been in New Delhi. Scott observed that that was a function of the high altitude of the city. They also were able to walk unhindered by beggars through the attractive central part of the city. The hotel, the embassy, and the bank were all near each other.

The visa interview was fairly easy, and Rakhi was told to expect its issuance within a week. Airline ticket reservations were not hard to make. Scott went back to his office, also downtown, while Rakhi went to the bank.

Mid-afternoon, they reconvened at the hotel. Over tea, Rakhi related that her reception at the bank was much friendlier than she had anticipated. Management there had been informed of her work with investors and foreign exchange matters in New Delhi, and they said there was a growing need to expand the Nairobi bank's foreign investment portfolio. India had wealthy potential investors. Being from India was an asset for Rakhi, especially in light also of the large and affluent Asian (Indian) community in Nairobi. A large part of her responsibility, if she got the job, would be to persuade the local Asian community to keep their money in Kenya and for Indians to invest in Kenya in light of recent actions in Uganda, where Idi Amin, now deposed, had kicked out Asians and appropriated their assets.

"Yeah," replied Scott. "I know I will need to go to Uganda soon after our return to learn more about that country and its relations with Kenya. Will the Kenyan government follow suit and throw out the Asians?"

"The bank does not think so, but they would want me to try to learn more."

Scott, in a moment of inspiration, exclaimed, "Let's go upstairs and make love to celebrate our achievements today!"

"Let's do! Then I can send a telegram to my parents in New Delhi to give them all the news."

They went upstairs, took a long and soapy shower together, and later ordered room service with more champagne. The telegram waited.

A week later, Scott and Rakhi were on the plane, flying straight through from Nairobi to New York, with just a stop in London. They were in New York a few days for Scott to check in with his head office. Senior editors there said his career was going strong after a series of excellent reports during his assignment to India. Thereafter, they headed to Washington, D.C., where Scott had a little one-bedroom condo in Arlington that he rented out.

It was Scott's plan to get the marriage license at the Arlington County Courthouse and then walk across the street to a lawyer's office for the civil marriage ceremony. He had once been a witness for a friend in that very law office. It was simple to get the license after a day's wait for blood test results.

Rakhi had invited her parents to attend and was prepared to wait on the ceremony until they could fly in. But they declined. Rakhi cried much of the day before the appearance at the courthouse. On that day, the two of them walked alone across the street from the courthouse. They were met at the basement level law office by Scott's graduate school friend Bob, who was there as a witness. A courtly older gentleman with a mane of totally white hair greeted Scott and Rakhi and did all he could to make them feel at ease and to emphasize the ceremonial importance of the occasion. He was an old-school Southern gentleman who did his job well. Rakhi cheered up a bit.

After the short ceremony, which left them both more somber than excited, they went down the street to the Key Bridge Marriott to have lunch. What to do on one's first day after a morning marriage? Rakhi wanted to see President John F. Kennedy's gravesite in Arlington National Cemetery, which was within walking distance of the hotel.

Standing on the knoll at the solemn gravesite that overlooked Memorial Bridge and the great monuments of the city, Scott wondered to himself, *Will I ever be good enough as a journalist to work in this city?* Thinking to herself, Rakhi wondered, *Could I ever feel at home in this city?* Neither shared these thoughts with the other.

Thereafter they walked across the nearby Key Bridge into Georgetown to have a drink or two at Clyde's, a cozy pub/restaurant Scott knew well. After several very dry martinis, Scott and Rakhi had their emotional equilibrium and mutual affection restored. Very woozy, they stumbled to a taxi to cross back over the bridge to their hotel and disappeared to their room. It had a dramatic view of the Washington skyline, but they did not notice it.

The next day they caught a flight from nearby National Airport to Tampa, the closest airport to Clearwater, Florida, where Scott's father and mother lived in a gated golf-themed community for senior citizens. His parents greeted Rakhi with affection but also with an undefined coolness or formality. They went to dinner at a popular seafood restaurant.

At the restaurant, matters were a bit stiff. After looking at the menu for a considerable time, Rakhi ordered steamed broccoli covered with cheese sauce.

"Don't you want anything else?" asked Scott's mother, Elizabeth.

"I'm vegetarian, so the broccoli will be fine," replied Rakhi.

Scott's parents exchanged glances. They had only heard about vegetarians but had no experience with anyone who ate only vegetables at a nice seafood restaurant.

"So, what part of India are you from, my dear?" asked Elizabeth, trying to find a common ground that did not exist.

"New Delhi," Rakhi replied, simply.

Elizabeth brightened, "Oh, is that where cows wander the streets? How do the cars not hit them? Or is the traffic mostly rickshaws?" Scott's dad tried to join the conversation, but his knowledge of India was meagre, and his mental image of India came from occasional black-and-white 1940s films that depicted restless natives causing trouble for the British, fans circulating slowly from high ceilings, and turbaned servants saying "Bwana, you want dinner now?" (or was it "Sahib want dinner?") He couldn't remember, and there were no bwanas or sahibs in South Dakota where he had grown up.

Rakhi did her best to convey a bit of the city life of her youth. "The streets of New Delhi are broad and filled with flowers in the medians, and there is hardly any traffic there. In the Old City of Delhi, the streets are quite narrow and filled with open-sir shops that sell everything, but especially fruits, vegetables, and sweets."

"If there are sweets for sale, there must be a lot of flies," noted her mother-in-law.

"Yes, in fact, there are," was all Rakhi could think of in reply.

After dinner, they returned to the parent's condo that overlooked the golf course's second green. "Does your father play golf?" asked Rakhi's father-in-law idly, not expecting a positive response.

"Well, he used to play quite a bit, but his hips are not so good now. His favorite sport at one time was polo."

"Oh." There was a pause as Scott's father digested this unexpected news.

"Well, I grew up on a horse in South Dakota," was his further response. "We didn't play polo though. The horses cut cattle, and we rode the range looking for strays."

Rakhi saw an opening, "I imagine blowing tumbleweed and rattlesnakes."

"Yeah, there were lots of rattlesnakes. One time I got caught in a patch of 'em. Lucky, I had on boots that went up to my mid-thighs. Otherwise, I would have been a goner."

"Goner?"

"Dead as a doornail."

The two couples thereafter said goodnight and retired to their respective bedrooms. In one bedroom, Elizabeth said, "Well, she seems nice enough. But how can she live on nothing but vegetables?" In the other bedroom, Rakhi said, "Well, I don't think I made a very good impression."

Scott felt sorry for his new bride. "You did the best you could. Keep in mind they have never met anyone from India, and certainly not a woman wearing a sari. I should have suggested you wear pants and a blouse."

"I'm sorry, Scott. At least I speak English and don't have a bone through my nose!" That was the end to a night not to remember.

The next day the newlyweds caught a flight from Tampa to London, glad to be moving along.

Thus ended their brief sojourn in the United States, and their modest marriage with no honeymoon. Their adventures, both personal and professional, were about to begin, however.

They had planned to stay a day in London so that Rakhi could go to the head office of Standard Chartered Bank. She emerged from the bank elated, having been told that her transfer to Nairobi was approved. She then went immediately to the Kenyan Embassy to change her visa from a tourist one to a work visa, the same visa Scott had. That procedure delayed their departure for Kenya by several days. They spent the time exploring London, a delight for Rakhi, and staying at the Dorchester Hotel, a huge splurge for Scott, who believed the success of any travel depended on the best of accommodations. He hoped that his days of staying at hostels behind the great hotels was over.

The two did not converse much on their eventual flight to Nairobi. They were immersed in thoughts of the future. Rakhi starting at the bank, Scott reporting for real duty at the newspaper, and both beginning life as a wedded couple.

Chapter Five

Trip to Uganda

Scott and Rakhi went back to the Intercon Hotel in Nairobi because it was the only residence they knew in the city, and it was close to her bank. They put off finding an apartment in the green suburban areas being developed not too far from the Central Business District. It was a bit of a shock for both to adjust to working again, and they agreed they didn't need the tension of finding an apartment in a city they did not know and could not navigate without a personal vehicle.

Just as had been predicted, Scott's boss Bob wanted Scott to fly over to Kampala, Uganda's capital, to try to learn more about the internal strife in that country and what it could mean to neighboring Kenya. Hardly settled but a few days into the hotel, Scott and Rakhi kissed goodbye and he headed to the airport. That pattern of farewells would become too familiar.

Landing at Entebbe and making his way into Kampala, Scott immediately could sense tension in the air. There was a palpable sense of fear as citizens watched the struggle of President Milton Obote to regain his former position as president in elections scheduled for early December 1980. Obote had to deal with the encroachments of diverse rebel elements in the many rural parts of the country, especially in the areas north of Kampala. Known as the Luwero Triangle, that region suffered from a persistent persecution of civilians in the growing struggle between various rebel groups and the forces of the Ugandan army loyal to Obote.

Scott met his local contact, a Ugandan journalist who seemed to know much about the confusing political scene. The journalist, Robert, suggested that Yoweri Museveni, a prominent rising leader from the Ugandan struggle with Tanzania some years earlier, was someone who should be interviewed. The problem was that Museveni was in the northern rural areas keeping himself hidden from government forces. Robert had confidence that his sources could lead him and Scott to Museveni.

Scott, Robert, a local operative said to be close to Museveni, and a hired driver with a tired range rover set off a few days later to drive north in search of the elusive Museveni and his rebel forces. The going was slow, principally because their vehicle had to stop every few miles at military checkpoints manned by army units who checked their papers very carefully. Scott noted that the average age of the checkpoint soldiers was probably not much beyond fifteen years. Some were hardly more than boys, but the older among them were armed with AK-47s, or some such military assault weapon. Scott made a note to try to learn where those weapons came from. Robert noted in an apprehensive voice after passing through the latest checkpoint that the principal reason they were progressing was Scott's American passport. The observation was not reassuring to Scott, who was beginning to think he had been foolhardy to set off on this venture.

As the miles passed, the landscape settled into a relatively flat region of fields and bush country. Few people were seen anywhere, and there was almost no other vehicle on the road. After a few hours, the local guide said they were approaching contested areas that were not safe. No more than a moment after those words were spoken, there was a loud clank from the engine, and the vehicle stalled. The driver opened the hood to discover that the main fan belt had broken.

There was no replacement. They were stranded on a lonesome road not far from dangerous territory. What were they going to do? The small group spent 20 minutes in useless speculation on a course of action when a four-door sedan approached from the north. Scott and Robert motioned for the vehicle to stop, which fortunately it did. Inside were several international aid workers coming back from contested areas just a few miles north. They said their destination was a small town a few miles south. They said under no circumstances should Scott and the others continue northward. The local guide lost his self-confidence and recommended his group join the newcomers at least as far as the town to the south. The aid workers agreed to make room, and the hapless driver was left with his Range Rover on the side of the road.

It was easy to get to the town and be dropped at the local bus stop. It was not so simple to wait for a bus, called in local parlance a matatu, which in fact was an old VW van. For a few pennies in local currency, the group purchased spaces in the van, which pulled out, bound for the next town south. Scott and his group really did not have seats. The locals in the vehicle moved closer together to make room. The matatu, sagging under the weight of a dozen passengers, limped out of the gathering area and headed south.

Not too many miles south, the matatu encountered the first military checkpoint. The boy guards checked documents closely and puzzled over the American passport and the white man inside the vehicle. Scott barely breathed. The guards conferred but then passed back the credentials and let the vehicle continue. A similar pattern developed a half-dozen more times before the vehicle made it into Kampala later in the afternoon.

Scott spent the next several days seeking out political observers to talk with, but in truth there were few individuals willing to meet, and they were too intimidated to say much of significance. Scott surmised that few residents of Kampala knew what was happening in the country. There would be a general election in some months, but the real balance of power was in the rural areas controlled by rebel groups who fought each other one day and allied with each other the next.

Scott was relieved to make his short flight back to Nairobi. While he had a mood piece to use as a reporting tool, it was not a hard-news story, and he suspected it would not be useful to return to Kampala in the near future.

Chapter Six

Down to Mombasa

Rakhi and Scott were relieved to be reunited after the week's separation. They made the most of their weekend together, once again in the same room at the Intercon Hotel. Rakhi was elated with her first week at the bank. She already sensed that the move from New Delhi would likely prove to be a career-enhancing one. The Nairobi branch had a vitality that the Delhi branch lacked, and its management did not seem as rigidly fixed. By contrast, Scott was already worrying that it would be tough to continue his status as a comer in the foreign correspondent world with his assignment in Nairobi. There was plenty of turmoil and potential violence in the region, but for the moment, Uganda was hard to decipher, and from what he could tell, internal Kenyan politics was relatively quiet and Bob, his superior, had that beat adequately covered.

Scott also sensed a slight shift in his relationship with Rakhi. She was not too happy personally with being left alone for a week in a hotel room. At the same time, in her new bank office, she saw many opportunities to explore, and it seemed she was going to be given the flexibility to pursue them. Scott, on the other hand, wondered if Nairobi was going to be a career-enhancing move, and the required separation from Rakhi was going to be a real hardship. On balance, it seemed Rakhi was enhancing her status in their relationship as the stronger one. That foundation had already been set; had it not been she who first proposed making love to him; had it not been she who had defied her parents and run off to Kashmir with him; had it not been she who followed him to Kenya?

It was clear too that they could not indefinitely stay in a hotel room. They needed to establish themselves in a community where there could be the comfort of a home and the prospect of neighbors. These concerns, though, would need to be put on the backburner because a trip outside of Nairobi was already pending. Bob wanted Scott to take a trip to Mombasa, Kenya's port city and the second-largest urban area in the country.

Scott learned that the most interesting manner, and certainly the most enjoyable way, to travel from Nairobi to Mombasa was on the overnight train, on which sleeping berths were available. He secured a reservation, kissed Rakhi goodbye just as she was arriving at the hotel after a day in the office and headed to the Nairobi rail station. From his window seat, he could see the generally flat savanna countryside as the train made its way south to Mombasa, but it soon enough became too dark to make out any landscape features. He made his way to the dining car. Maybe he could strike up a conversation with a Kenyan or two. He did have a pleasant conversation over dinner, but not with a black African Kenyan, but a Kenyan citizen nonetheless.

His companion was an older, courtly, soft-spoken gentleman who was a Kenyan-born Indian (known as an Asian in the East African context). His family had come from India as small merchants in the early part of the twentieth century. Mr. Patel recounted how the family had prospered, and he had had a good career as a barrister, after graduating decades before in law from Lincoln's Inn in London.

"In the years immediately after Kenyan independence, those who practiced law had a great deal of business to protect the Asian community from attempts by the new government to take over their businesses," Patel explained.

"I just came back from my first trip to Uganda. There are few Asians left in that country after Idi Amin kicked them out and stole their assets a few years back," Scott replied, showing off his new knowledge of East Africa.

"Do you think that could happen here?" he asked of Mr. Patel.

Patel considered for a long moment. "No, I don't think so. The Asian community here has become skillful in ingratiating itself with President Moi and his party. And Moi seems to understand that without the Asian business community in Kenya, the economy might collapse."

"That's not to say that what Asians fear most cannot be exploited for the benefit of the black African community."

Patel went on, "All major Asian business families are worried that the ax could fall any day. But they are fairly confident they would have some advance notice. To be on the safe side, everyone has a bug-out suitcase packed to leave the country on a moment's notice, and many Asians also have resident status in the U.K., and a goodly portion of their money is in British banks, or American ones."

Scott made a note to pass this to Rakhi, although he suspected she already knew this information.

"Why are you going to Mombasa?" asked Patel.

"I want to explore the historic parts of the city and learn something about it as a port city for East Africa. I understand also that it is a melting pot of Africans, Asians, Arabs, and Europeans. That's a rare combination."

"You are right. And the four groups you mention co-exist peacefully, most of the time. The Arab influence is strong; make certain to get to the old harbor to see the dhows sailing in from the Persian Gulf. Life in the old harbor and in the adjoining old city hasn't changed much over the centuries."

Patel added, almost as an afterthought, "In that mix of ethnicities and cultures that live together in Mombasa, there is also the white Kenyan group, that is, either the pioneer settlers who came from the U.K. as farmers upcountry and many of whom have now retired to the coast, or their grown children. The latter are a conflicted lot. They don't belong in Kenya, which is not welcoming, but they don't belong back in the U.K. either."

Warming to his topic, Patel said, "Come have lunch with me tomorrow at the Mombasa Club. It is at the seaward edge of the old city, on a choice spot where there is a good view of the dhows in the old harbor. And you will see many of the elderly white Kenyans, who spend much of their time at the club reading the dated British newspapers or dozing in the overstuffed chairs."

"That would be very fine! Thank you." Scott and Patel exchanged cards, and the luncheon was set. Scott went back to a berth made up for him much cheered up by the prospect of exploring an exotic city the next day.

Chapter Seven

The Mombasa Club, Fort Jesus, and the Old Town

As he stepped from the train, the heat and humidity of the Kenyan coast hit Scott with a shocking, oppressive force. Nairobi was pleasant at an altitude of about six thousand feet, but Mombasa at sea level and right on the equator was vividly tropical. Storm clouds hovered over the city, to be broken by searing sunshine moments later. Scott's shirt was drenched within minutes, but he was excited too. A simple poster, one of hundreds put up haphazardly on the train station walls by former passengers, added to his pleasure. His favorite was one stating "Visit Wall Drug." Scott knew the reference was to the famous drug store in Wall, South Dakota, not far from the lands his relatives still farmed.

Joe, a local African journalist and contact of Scott's newspaper, stuck out his hand and in a friendly voice said, "You must be Scott. Welcome to Mombasa! I've got a car; where are you staying?"

"The White Castle Hotel. It's nearby, right?"

"Yes. It is in the middle of the city."

The two of them drove the short distance to the White Castle, an old, large and impressive structure, white-painted, with shaded balconies off spacious rooms with large ceiling fans and beds framed by mosquito netting.

"Ernest Hemingway stayed here in the 1930s when he came to Kenya on a safari," Joe said proudly. Scott immediately liked the large dark lobby cooled by circulating fans.

"I have a busy day planned for you with shipping agents and with the director of the port," Joe noted. "You can't understand Mombasa without appreciating the role of shipping here."

"Great. Let me have a cool shower first and I'll meet you in the bar."

True to his word, Scott met a British and a German shipping agent, each of whom said the lifeblood not just of Kenya but of Rwanda and Uganda passed through the busy port, modernized and deepened by the U.S. Navy in recent years to accommodate the periodic American warship visits.

"But what about the dhows sailing down from the Persian Gulf?" asked Scott, recalling his train conversation with Patel.

The African director of the port dismissed the dhows with a wave of his hand. "They come into the old port, on the other side of the point dominated by Fort Jesus. They are more a curiosity these days, not vital to our economy. But they are picturesque. From the Mombasa Club veranda, one can see them coming in now from Dubai and elsewhere from the Persian Gulf."

"If you wish to see a spectacular contrast to the sailing dhows, come back next month when a U.S. Navy battlegroup will be making a port call. Nothing like an aircraft carrier in port, with a half-dozen destroyers accompanying and 5,000 men on the streets."

Scott made a mental note to return, maybe with Rakhi, for the U.S. warships. Might be a good feature story.

In the gathering dusk, Joe took Scott around to meet a Kenyan political leader named Ahmed, who controlled the city on behalf of President Moi. They went around to Ahmed's home on the edge of the port. Sitting in the deepening gloom (*Doesn't he believe in lamps?* thought Scott), the three discussed local politics until it was virtually impossible to see each other across the room. Finally, acknowledging the blackness, Ahmed said, "It's getting dark. Let's go upstairs." Ahmed added with a bit of drama, "There may be women there."

Scott followed, wondering what he was in for. The women turned out to be Ahmed's wife and daughter, who served tea.

Afterwards, Joe dropped Scott at the hotel, where Scott dined alone in the virtually empty dining room. He wanted to wander the streets after dinner, but they were dark, deserted, and forbidding. He retreated to his room and climbed under the mosquito netting. He called Rakhi, and by a miracle got connected.

"God, I miss you, my darling!" Scott exclaimed.

"I need you," said Rakhi. "I can't take this lonesome life. First Uganda, now Mombasa. I need you here beside me, kissing me good-night."

"I'll be back in a few days, and I have an idea. In a month, come with me on a return visit to Mombasa. I saw a Standard Chartered bank in town. Big place. Surely, you need to visit it."

"And I am told the beach resorts near the city are spectacular," he added.

"I will see what I can do to come along. Maybe there is business for me in Mombasa. You like beach resorts?" Rakhi asked.

"Sure, don't you?"

"I don't know how to swim, and I don't want to be darkened by the sun at the beach. But I am sure it is nice to walk at dawn or dusk on the beach."

"Okay, darling, we'll do that. I love you so much."

"I love you too. Come back quickly!"

The next day at noon, Scott met his new friend Patel at the Mombasa Club lobby. The club was in fact on the edge of the old city, next to the imposing Fort Jesus, built by the Portuguese in the seventeenth century to guard the approach to the harbor, now the "old" harbor.

Patel took Scott through a reception room to the veranda, which had a number of tables set for lunch. The warm moist wind blowing off the harbor, and indeed the open ocean clearly visible in the distance, was intoxicating to Scott, who had a life-long fascination with the sea. The seaward edge of the luncheon veranda hung over the rocks immediately below. To the right were the ramparts of Fort Jesus, and to the left were the docks with the narrow alleys of the old city leading away from the docks. The sailing dhows were tied up, and a few had workers hauling off bagged cargo by hand.

Patel said he came to the club every day for lunch, walking from his nearby office. He always had a table on the left side of the veranda, and facing out to sea, under an awning that could protect diners from the occasional showers that blew up in the rainy season, which they were now in. There were billowing dark clouds over the sea at that moment.

"What is your primary interest in Mombasa?" Patel asked.

"Well, I learned about the importance of shipping here, and I heard a bit of political news at a meeting last night."

"Let me tell you, there are only two important political stories here, and neither one will be accessible to you as a foreign journalist."

"Why not?" asked Scott.

"Because they are hidden from Westerners in general. One has to do with the growing anger in the Muslim community over Kenya's close ties to the U.S. The imams who preach in the mosques rail against American hatred of Islam at Friday prayers in the mosques, but only devout Muslims hear the message, and neither the African community, which is largely Christian, nor the white community here is aware. The imams are also angry over the influx of European tourists at all these beach resorts springing up."

"What's the other political story?"

"It is the tight control the ruling political party has on the country, and the ruthless methods they use against anyone seen as a challenge. You will not hear that story either unless you seek out those who have been arrested and beaten by authorities."

"How can one meet such individuals?" asked Scott.

Patel answered without a moment of hesitation. "There are little notices on the back page of the newspaper that tell who has been re-leased in recent days from jail. The story gives the name and the offense. It might be possible to look up some of those named, if they are willing to talk to you. I know about this because of my interest in human rights abuses," Patel added, bringing the serious part of the luncheon conver-sation to a close.

Brightening, he exclaimed, "There's a lady you should meet!" He rose to meet the white woman entering the veranda.

"Erol, you should meet a new acquaintance of mine, Scott. He is newly arrived as a foreign newspaperman."

Erol was a charming, middle-aged woman with an engaging smile, alert eyes, and a gracious manner. Her accent indicated she was British. She said she was married to a Polish architect and they had just moved to the coast from Nairobi.

"Are you here for some time?" Erol asked.

"No, just a few days. I am posted up in Nairobi. But I hope to come back with some frequency, especially with my wife. I think it would be enjoyable to drive up the coast a bit. I hear it is exotic."

"It is, but dangerous these days. There are those who will want to hijack your car, to say nothing of murderous Somali bands in the northern reaches.

"But should you want to explore north, my husband and I have a centuries-old Swahili house in the middle of the old town on the island of Lamu. You would be welcome to use it."

Scott made a note of that offer.

As the three departed the club, Patel noted Scott was wearing a wrist amulet. "That's called a Rakhi. You must have gotten it as a gift."

"I did, from my wife of the same name."

"Very special," Patel noted. They agreed to keep in touch. Scott said goodbye to Erol as well, pledging to get in touch when next at the coast.

As Scott walked to the entrance of the club drive and started to turn left to go up the ramp to the Fort Jesus entrance, his attention was drawn to two African men loitering at the club entrance. He had seen them when he entered the gate, at the same spot.

After climbing the ramparts and appreciating how the Portuguese defenders had created what must have been a solid barrier to anyone wishing to enter Mombasa by sea, it was getting toward sunset. Scott was loath to leave the prevailing warm wind coming from the ocean, but he planned to walk into the old town and find a little Swahili restaurant where Patel said he could sit on a sidewalk table and sample Swahili fried fish. Scott noted with relief that the two loitering Africans were gone.

Scott asked a few pedestrians and found the eating establishment, rough and simple, but the fish was good. As he was finishing with sweet tea, Scott checked his watch and realized it was time to head back to the White Castle. He had been warned not to stay out after dark on the city streets. There was nothing to do at this hour but walk. There were no taxis or other transport in the old town. The distance was less than a mile.

Nearing his hotel, Scott saw one of the Africans he had seen earlier now lounging on the hotel veranda. When Scott looked at him directly, the man pretended to be absorbed with a newspaper in his hand. Scott knew he was being followed.

The next day, Scott explored the beach area developing north of the town, which itself was on an island attached to the mainland by several short bridges. One could not see the resorts from the two-lane road, but signs directed drivers where to turn to the right and head the short distance to the beach area, which when not developed was dense foliage—primeval jungle. Scott had picked up a few brochures at the in-town White Castle Hotel, a fixture from colonial days before anyone dreamed of tearing through the jungles to get to the beaches.

He chose the closest resort to town. The road actually led him through an elegant suburb of walled estates before ending at the hotel. Scott strolled through the lobby, circled around the pool, and headed to the beach. It was a bit narrow but had clean white sand that was too hot to venture onto in late morning. To his surprise, he found no surf because the beach was protected by a coral reef some two hundred meters offshore. He could see thundering waves breaking on the reef. Billowing dark clouds hung on the horizon over the Indian Ocean. Scott determined he would need to bring Rakhi to this hotel.

He had a recommendation that a nearby restaurant, around the point to the right from the hotel and along the bay opposite the old harbor, was the best place to have lunch. He learned later that travel writers from around the world called the Tamarind the restaurant with the most dramatic views, the best food, and the most polished service on the East Coast of Africa, if not the entire continent. Scott ordered a bottle of wine and lingered away the hours, initially feeling guilty he was not working and later rationalizing he was absorbing local culture that would turn into an innocent feature about beach resort development and the good life on the Kenyan coast. He added the Tamarind to the list of places to bring Rakhi. That vow did not come to pass.

Chapter Eight

Prisoner Information and Personal Intimidation

Back in Nairobi, Scott related his concern to Bob that he had been followed on his final day in Mombasa. After checking with other correspondents about their experiences, Bob reported that no other colleague had such a story. Scott surmised that his visit to the political leader in Mombasa had put him on someone's radar. Rakhi did not like the episode at all, but Scott felt he had an obligation to tell her.

Bob's advice to Scott was for him and Rakhi to take standard evasive tactics, such as varying their travel paths and timing to and from the office. Bob thought it wise that Rakhi not walk from the hotel to the bank. Since neither of them saw evidence of being followed, they did little to vary their routines and their concerns abated.

Scott tried to put into action Patel's suggestion that he look up recently released prisoners. It wasn't hard to find a few names, but it was extremely difficult to track down those released, who were not prominent citizens. Their crimes were variously listed as thievery, assault, or resisting arrest. It was even more difficult to find someone willing to meet a journalist.

With the help of a local African assistant in the office, Scott found one individual willing to meet with him, but with unnerving precautions imposed by the fellow. Come alone. No printing of information. Scott met the fellow behind a bicycle repair shop in a part of the city he should not have been in, day or night. The meeting was at twilight.

From the formerly imprisoned man, Scott learned of police abuse, especially in the first day or two of detention. Slapping and punching was standard. What the fellow did not expect was beating of the soles of his feet with rods. He was also forced to stand for hours, or squat for hours until it was excruciatingly painful. Authorities wanted to know names of associates who might harbor unkindly thoughts about the government.

"Why did police single you out?" asked Scott.

In coarse English Scott found hard to follow, he was told the man had been meeting with low-level political operatives opposed to the main political party. All innocent behavior of friends with mutual interests. They weren't plotting violence. The man claimed he did not give up names. He was held for about a month and then released without any formal charges, despite the newspaper account that he had been arrested for thievery. Scott departed in complete darkness to a waiting car driven by an office assistant. He was darned pleased the car was there. The neighborhood did not look or feel friendly; he feared being mugged for his watch and wallet, at the least.

Scott started meeting more individuals, usually at night, with similar stories. He began to see a pattern of official intimidation of political opposition figures. Bob encouraged Scott to draft a piece for the Stateside editors.

One story became several. Scott was developing primary information on a form of human rights abuse that his editors found worthwhile. Some of his reporting began to be repeated in local newspapers. Scott kept an eye out for possible surveillance, but nothing was evident.

One morning a typed and unsigned note came to the office. It said, **"Lay off your reporting."** No one saw it delivered, but it did not come through the postal system.

Bob took the note to a police contact he knew. Scott was called in later by the local police for a meeting. Bob accompanied him.

"We take threatening notes like this seriously," the detective said. "We are proud of our free press and will not tolerate such threats to journalists, especially American ones."

"At the same time, you are being misled by these accounts of police abuse. We do not beat or otherwise abuse those arrested. Nor do we hold them for lengthy periods without charge."

The meeting concluded, "Stay away from lowlifes who will tell you any story they think will interest you. We know these kinds of people."

Bob thought it might be useful for Scott to get out of town for a bit, and fortunately, a U.S. Navy aircraft carrier battle group was about to pay an official port call in Mombasa. That event could provide an innocent feature story about a port city inundated with thousands of sailors looking for a good time. It was said that ladies of the night were already converging on Mombasa from throughout Kenya and from neighboring countries to help entertain the sailors.

Rakhi received permission from her managers to visit Mombasa. They liked her idea to search out some of the more important Asian businessmen on the coast. Such outreach was not common to banking officials. They did not realize that Rakhi was emulating Scott's gumshoe efforts to track down those in the know, or in her case, those with money. Scott planned to introduce her to Patel, the Mombasa barrister.

They bought a second-hand Range Rover and secured a parking spot in the hotel basement. Scott wanted the freedom to explore the rural areas, and he especially wanted to drive to Mombasa rather than take an overnight train from whose windows nothing but the absolute blackness of the African savanna was visible outside the train windows for most of the journey. He convinced Rakhi that it was safer in the countryside than in the city and that driving a vehicle on the roads would be safe. She was dubious. She had heard of an elderly American missionary couple who had been killed on the highway by those who wanted their car.

The night before their planned road trip to Mombasa, Rakhi and Scott lay in bed and held each other for comfort. She was growing fearful, both in the city and in the country. He gently massaged her, putting lotion on her arms and legs. She massaged him also. Together, they renewed their affection, which had been tested in recent times with their increasing work and then growing personal fears. She succumbed to his touch and was more peaceful thereafter.

Chapter Nine

Encounter on the Road to Mombasa

Just after daybreak, Scott and Rakhi drove out of Nairobi, glad to leave the city behind. There was almost no traffic on the Mombasa road, which was two lanes but well maintained. They drove through savanna, not cultivated land. While they hoped to see some wildlife, they were disappointed. About halfway through the three-hundred-mile journey, the rudimentary map showed a secondary road to the left that made a large semi-circle before rejoining the main road, maybe seventy-five miles south. The thin line on the map indicated the road went through the Tsavo East National Game Preserve. Surely there would be wildlife to see. They approached the road carefully, hesitating to turn onto it, but the road was gravel and no problem for the four-wheel-drive range rover.

At first, the terrain was the same savanna environment seen from the main road. That is, it was grassland with occasional clumps of trees, including the dramatic baobabs with their enormous thick trunks and spreading branches. Scott knew the trees could live hundreds of years. There were herds of zebra and gazelles that paid no mind to the lone vehicle. Rakhi kept a sharp eye out for elephants but to no avail. The road became narrower, and eventually dwindled to but a path, yet still a discernable one.

They debated whether to turn back. They had forty or more miles invested. The weather was clear and dry, the vehicle was strong, they were young, and they pushed forward.

The path came to the bank of a dry riverbed. It was only six to eight feet down the bank to the sandy bottom, but Scott got out to test how firm the ground was. He decided it was all right to inch down the embankment. He put the rover into first gear and crept down the slope. Rakhi held her breath. The riverbed was firm sand, and they continued creeping along the path. One could see that another vehicle had journeyed along this route in recent days. Then for some reason the path turned upward to breech the top of the bank again.

Scott stopped again for a moment. Rakhi implored, "Why on earth are we here?"

Scott eased up the clutch and moved the rover forward so slightly, fearful otherwise that his wheels might sink into the soft sand. The car slowly moved forward and climbed the bank. At the top, the path, now more discernable, led into a grove of bamboo. They crept through the bamboo until they came upon a small clearing, more an enclosure within the towering bamboo stalks.

There were about thirty water buffalo munching the bamboo in the tiny enclosure. The animals, for all their natural instincts, had not heard the coming vehicle. They looked up in unison, startled, and snorted menacingly at the car not ten feet from them. Scott stopped the vehicle instantly.

"Don't look them in the eye!" whispered Scott. He had heard that that could be deadly when confronting wild animals in Kenya, and water buffalo could be the deadliest because of their unpredictability. His breathing virtually stopped. Rakhi's hand gripped his leg, out of sight of the buffalo eyes. No living thing moved. The animals stared at the vehicle, evaluating their immediate threat. The humans tried to fix their eyes somewhere above the eyes of the animals.

The buffalo closest to the vehicle snorted menacingly. He took a few steps toward the vehicle until he was within five feet of the front bumper. Then the animal stared at them again. Scott, heart pounding, sweat pouring down his face, thought frantically that the animal's horns could penetrate the doors of the vehicle as though they were cardboard. The horns could destroy the radiator; slash the tires.

Rakhi faintly whispered, "We're helpless!" For a split second, Scott thought of sounding the horn. Bad idea, he immediately realized.

The animals continued to stare at the vehicle, apparently unsure whether it was a threat. How long went by? Five minutes? Ten minutes? Then what apparently was the buffalo leader and the one closest to the vehicle lowered his head and picked up a bamboo shoot in his teeth. He looked back up and stared with bloodshot eyes directly at Scott. He stopped munching the shoot and took a step closer.

A thought flashed through Scott's mind: *Why die so passively? Maybe I should back up?* But his leg had begun to tremble, and he didn't think he could manage the clutch.

Tension broke. The lead buffalo put his head down to graze. The other animals started to do the same. They did not leave the clearing. The vehicle remained stranded. Scott could not go forward, and he instantly decided not to back away and encounter the riverbank. They waited. Ten minutes stretched into twenty. Then the buffalo began to wander through the bamboo, crushing the twenty-foot high stalks as they moved. Within another ten minutes, they were gone.

Scott put the car in gear and moved forward slightly, his trembling leg somewhat cooperating. No buffalo ahead. He kept moving, and the path became wider as they emerged from the bamboo grove. They gathered a bit of speed. Five minutes later they had left the bamboo and the dry riverbed behind. Scott stopped the car, largely because his legs were still hard to control. Rakhi was crying almost silently.

He stepped out of the car to stretch his cramped leg muscles and control the trembling. Rakhi stayed firmly within the car and said nothing.

He got back into the car and began driving. There was silence between them. The path became a proper gravel road. Rakhi had regained her composure, but not her good humor. She turned to Scott and said, evenly, "We were trapped, and not a soul knows we took this detour. We could have been killed and left to rot. You are impulsive, too much so. I am a fool not to speak up."

Scott listened impassively to her words. He knew Rakhi was right, dead right. They drove on in silence until they reached the tarmac of the Mombasa road. They turned to the left and drove the remaining eighty miles to the city, hardly sharing a word.

Chapter Ten

A U.S. Carrier Battle Group in Port

The American aircraft carrier *Midway* and nine support ships, including several destroyers and one cruiser, had pulled into Mombasa for a three-day port visit to refuel, garner fresh food, show the American flag to a friendly nation, and give the 5,000 sailors a bit of free time. Hundreds of hours had gone into planning the visit, which would include the painting of an orphanage inside and out, free hot dogs and hamburgers for sailors at the local Missions to Seamen, a humming business at the portside bars, a fancy reception at the American Consul's residence, and VIP visits to the mayor by the rear admiral of the battlegroup and the carrier captain. While the Midway was one of the older carriers in the U.S. fleet, its presence in the African port was awe-inspiring to locals and expats alike.

Scott was pleased to be covering the event, thought to be a good feature story. Rakhi was in town to meet Asian money, which she did, aided by the fact that many in that group were at the Consul's outdoor reception, which featured the playing of the carrier's band on the patio surrounding the pool. She found friendly smiles everywhere she turned. A banker from Nairobi had never come to Mombasa in living memory to court investors, or in this case, to try to reassure them that their existing investments in Kenya were safe. It did not hurt that the banker was a stunning beauty who could speak to the Asians—that is, the Indian community—in their own language.

True to Scott's vow from his first Mombasa trip, he booked a seaview room at the Nyali Beach Hotel, only a few hundred yards from the Consul's residence. They could hear the band playing when they left the resort's gate and strolled over to the residence. After the reception, Scott and Rakhi returned to their hotel room, which had a view of the Indian Ocean with its coral reef and crashing breakers from the open ocean. They made plans to walk on the beach at dawn. Until then, they snuggled in each other's arms, reconciled after the tension in the game preserve, and slept the way lovers should sleep after making love.

The next morning after the beach walk in the early dawn coolness and a fine breakfast on the resort's patio overlooking the pool, Rakhi dressed fit to kill in a light blue silk sari and headed for the first of her day's meetings.

Scott went first to the Missions to Seamen, a freshly painted white building near the port. The mission had a chapel for those who wanted to thank the Lord for keeping them safe at sea, and at noon, the court-yard was packed with cheerful, clean-cut sailors eating free sliders—what Scott learned were burgers provided by the carrier. It was a wholesome environment, meant as a contrast to the dozens of bars and dirt cheap hotels nearby where sailors could be entertained day and night by local girls who wanted nothing but to separate the men from their money, for as little as an hour or two of affection given to those made foolishly lonesome by weeks at sea. Too often the sailors took away more than affection from their brief assignations with the girls, who knew little to nothing about venereal disease and the men who often were too impatient to worry about protection, despite the graphic lectures they had received before the boats came into the harbor.

Scott sought out the Porthole, a place he had heard was popular with the sailors. Even at noon, the bar was crammed. The sailors were generally well-behaved, and the girls were friendly and generally attractive.

"Hi, buy a girl a beer?" asked an African girl with smooth skin and long legs.

"Sure. Pretty busy here." Scott had no idea how to converse with a port-city prostitute, or what he assumed she was.

"Yes, we are happy have American men here today. You wish go upstairs?"

"Let's talk for a bit first."

"Okay," she replied, glancing around and clearly losing enthusiasm for Scott.

"Where are you from?" Scott asked.

"I'm from Kampala—do you know where is?" she asked, bored.

"Yes, I've been there. It's a long way away. What do you do there?"

"I work in office as secretary. I come for ships. I make more money in three days here than month in my office. Now let's go upstairs."

"No, I need to leave."

"You owe me something for my time, buster. I don't chat for nothing."

"Fair enough. Here's a hundred shillings."

Scott left the bar with a nugget of information for his pending story. Before the day was out, he would have more than a tale of a girl from Kampala looking for a purse stuffed with easy cash.

That night, he got a midnight call from the chaplain at the Missions to Seamen. The chaplain gave him a scoop. A local lady had been found dead at the Porthole, in the company of three sailors who said she had passed out. They didn't know why. The chaplain said if Scott wanted a story about the ship visit, this was it.

Scott grabbed a taxi at the hotel front door and had the driver take him to the Porthole. The driver didn't seem fazed; apparently it was not that uncommon for male guests at the luxury beach hotel to go slumming at the port's most notorious bar late at night. The girl's body was still in the room. The local authorities seemed paralyzed by the death. Scott learned no African would touch a dead body. The American Consul showed up too, about the same time as MPs from the carrier. Scott was on the periphery. No one paid him any attention. The girl was not the one he had met at noon. The girl's body was finally taken away to the morgue for a postmortem. Later Scott heard she had died of a drug overdose. The three sailors were taken into custody for questioning, with foul play suspected.

Scott hastened back to the Nyali Beach hotel and wrote a dispatch quickly. His story was in Kenya's morning papers, and also his own publication back in New York. The theme was the port city packed with ladies of the night, and the dangers that they encountered. His story caught the unfavorable attention of those who had been shadowing him in Mombasa and Nairobi. A considerable personal price was building to be paid for Scott's growing reputation as a muck-raking foreign reporter.

Chapter Eleven

North to Lamu

Before leaving Mombasa to drive north along the coast of Kenya in the direction of Somalia, Scott checked in with Erol, the British lady he had met on his luncheon visit to the Mombasa Club. She had impulsively offered him and Rakhi the use of her family's Swahili house in the middle of the old town of Lamu, an island a few miles off the Kenyan coast and not far south of Somalia. Lamu, Erol had said, was a living museum, a slice of Muslim life from medieval times on the remote island.

Erol and her husband graciously followed through on their offer, somehow sending word to Lamu that the houseboy there should expect two foreign guests to knock on the door (provided that the door could be found in that ancient little town.)

Before going, Rakhi sternly said to Scott, "I am all for adventure, but I hear driving the 180 miles to the ferry landing for Lamu is a sketchy endeavor that we should reconsider. The final 90 miles are on a remote gravel road. No one can help us if there is trouble, and there are reports of Somali bandits who prey on solitary road travelers and foreign missionaries in that area."

Rakhi was right to voice caution. A few months back a compound of Catholic nuns had been raided in the northern regions, with all killed, presumably by Somali bandits. Scott was indeed foolhardy. But he craved adventure and a good story, and he imagined there would be a good feature on life in Lamu. He needed an innocent tourist story or two to counteract his growing portfolio of exposing human rights abuses.

Scott first drove the eighty miles to Malindi, a small coastal town and ancient port. The road paralleled the coast by a half-mile or so, going through dense foliage that separated the road from the rugged coast with its coral cliffs.

The city had been a rival in sea trade with Mombasa for centuries and in the sixteenth century had the important patronage of the Portuguese. In fact, Vasco de Gama himself had had erected a pillar on a coral bluff above the ocean to mark his stop there in 1498. By the time of the visit of Scott and Rakhi, the port town was evolving into an international tourist haven with a unique flair—it was home to a sizable Italian community. The town had the best trattorias in Africa, the best bakeries, and some very well-designed resorts. The rumors were that Italian high-rollers had built dramatic mansions on the coral heights along the Malindi coast. The rumors suggested that the high rollers were mafia who used Malindi as a safe haven. Scott made another mental note to explore Malindi and the Italian influence on a subsequent trip. That vow, like the one to take Rakhi to the Tamarind in Mombasa, did not come to pass because of events beyond his control.

In Malindi, Scott paid a courtesy call on the local government office there, the Deputy Commissioner (DC). The friendly official welcomed Scott and Rakhi to Malindi but cautioned both that the road to the ferry landing was indeed inherently unsafe. It seemed clear the DC did not want to be responsible for two Americans. He said he would contact his DC colleague on Lamu Island and requested that Scott check in with him soon after arrival.

Scott, undeterred, urged his reluctant wife back to the rover to begin the 90-mile leg of the trip. The road was gravel but reasonably well-maintained. There was not another vehicle on the road for the entire journey. Scott kept his worries to himself that he would throw a fan belt, as had happened in northern Uganda on his earlier trip there. Half-way through the journey, they noticed that the road was black in the far distance but became a familiar brown color closer to the vehicle. Scott noticed in the mirror that the road behind him was black in the distance also. Why was that?

They discovered that they weren't the only living beings on the road. What initially had seemed like blackness on the road turned out to be hundreds, if not thousands, of baboons sitting on the road, moving only grudgingly as the vehicle approached, and regrouping immediately behind the car as it passed. How deferential would these animals be if the car stopped? Neither Scott nor Rakhi wanted to have another encounter with wild animals.

Rakhi was loyal to Scott, but to herself she began to wonder why she had hooked up with this American. For his part, Scott had a growing sense of guilt for exposing his new wife to unnecessary danger. As before, neither expressed these inner thoughts to the other.

They reached the ferry terminus, a mere dirt parking area near a pier for the local ferry. A small group of boys ran to their car, each boy begging to be the guardian of the car after Scott and Rakhi departed on the waiting ferry. Trusting to blind faith, Scott gave a boy a handful of shillings with a promise of more to guard the vehicle while they were in Lamu. The boy saluted.

With a hundred other local Kenyans and Swahili Arabs, they boarded the ferry, which became quickly overloaded. It cast off. The boat's gunnels were inches about the water. If trouble came, Scott knew it didn't matter if he could swim because all the ferry goers, who no doubt could not swim, would climb on top of him in the water if the ferryboat capsized. He drew as close as he could to Rakhi, who had already sized up the inherent danger. She did not have the advantage even of knowing how to swim. Her face white, her gaze fixed on the water ahead, her knuckles gripping the gunnel like vices, Rakhi said silent prayers to Shiva, her protector among the Hindu gods.

The island was only a few miles distant and they arrived safely. They were greeted by boys and old men with donkeys who wanted Rakhi to ride one as they made their way into the depths of the ancient town. Scott had the coordinates of Erol's house on a piece of paper. A local boy guided them, but without the donkey. Rakhi was not about to be seen riding one. With assistance, it was not hard to find the house, a centuries-old traditional structure on a narrow street. The houseboy expected them and showed them to a stuffy upstairs bedroom but suggested they might prefer to sleep on the roof where it was cooler. Two charpoys were there for them. It was the first time for either of them to sleep on a charpoy, a traditional South Asian low wooden structure with intertwined rope to support one's body. It wasn't so uncomfortable, and the coolness of the evening was inviting. They made love with only the stars as witnesses.

"I am sorry I was sharp with you after the water buffalo experience," Rakhi volunteered in the tender moments after lovemaking.

"I love you so," she added, caressing his cheek tenderly and running her finger along his lips.

"I love you too and don't even recall a sharp word. I must remember my first duty is to protect you," Scott replied solemnly. They fell asleep peacefully and were awakened at dawn by the muezzin's Azan call to prayer from the adjoining mosque. Scott loved the exotic sound of the call to prayer, and Rakhi appreciated its poetic intonation, although neither of them could understand the Arabic words.

At mid-morning they walked through the narrow streets of the medieval town, asking periodically of men how to find the Lamu Deputy Commissioner's office. He graciously received them and provided tea. The DC clearly was relieved they had survived the road trip. He said Lamu had not changed much in a thousand years and that no motor vehicle but his official one was allowed on the small island. Donkeys were the only means of transport. He added proudly that the late nineteenth-century British adventure writer H. Rider Haggard had completed his most famous novel, *King Solomon's Mines*, while on the island in the 1880s when his brother had been deputy commissioner in that colonial period. (Scott looked up this account later—he learned the story about the drafting of the novel on Lamu Island apparently was not accurate, even if it was widely believed among the British in Kenya and by the DC himself, an African official who had a hundred years after Haggard's time responsibilities probably not so different.) Scott had loved the novel as a teenager and credited it with inspiring him to seek out foreign lands and adventures.

Erol had been right about Lamu. It was an African-Arab island for-gotten by history and the contemporary world. A few backpackers roamed the streets. There were more donkeys in the old city than people, it seemed: The women were covered head to toe, and the men were indifferent to the occasional foreigner in the streets. Despite the profoundly alien atmosphere, with no knowledge of Swahili, no means of movement but to walk, no apparent sanitation for food at local stalls, trusting luck that the hot tea they drank would not give them dysentery or hepatitis, Scott and Rakhi felt safe enough, although Rakhi dreaded the thought of the ferry ride back to the mainland.

It was the last time in fact that they would be safe in Kenya. In the coming months, Scott would have occasion to try to prove his ability to protect Rakhi, and to hate himself for his inadequacy.

Chapter Twelve

Another Personal Threat

Back in Nairobi, Rakhi returned to her bank with many useful coastal Asian contacts, which senior management greatly appreciated. Privately, her superiors thanked their lucky stars that Rakhi had dropped out of the heavens to join their bank from the New Delhi branch. They considered sending her on foreign business trips; India was at the top of the list, as was the U.K. The greatest concentration of Asian money was in Bombay, but a close second was in London. Rakhi seemed the young executive who could most successfully interact with the important potential investors in each of those cities.

Scott was riding high too. His report on the U.S. naval visit to Mombasa and the death of the young woman got good reviews, and his feature on Muslim life in Lamu added a colorful flair to his growing repertoire. He went back to work to expose human rights violations in Kenya, notably in the police forces.

Some months later, another anonymous note appeared at his office. It said simply, **"Enough—go back to your own country. No more poking around in matters you do not understand."**

Bob and Scott returned to the Nairobi police headquarters. Officials there assured the two that all would be done to catch the culprits who were responsible for what they called "amateur intimidation." The police suggested it might be better for Scott to write more features about the colorful locations of Kenya. Had he considered the Rift Valley? Or maybe it would be good to write about tourist safaris to the Masai Mara and the wildlife of the larger Serengeti plain.

The letter also raised concerns at the newspaper's head office in New York. Plans began to be discussed, unknown to Scott, that he may need to be reassigned to another country.

Scott thought he detected an African shadowing his movements, but he could not be certain. If it was true, the man was more sophisticated than the two who had watched him on his first trip to Mombasa. Scott reported this to his superiors and to the police. They determined that for his safety, it would be better that he continue to reside at the Intercon Hotel, where there was security that would be enhanced. He and Rakhi had been considering a rental property in the new Westfields development, where the neighborhood clusters included gated communities. Police advised against such a move. As a precaution, Scott's office provided him a dedicated car and driver. Rakhi's bank did the same.

The two lived in a state of low-level tension for several more months. Scott continued to develop contacts among recently released prisoners, a few of whom were outright political opponents of the ruling party and the government. Scott felt his professional development demanded he not relent when he had solid information.

Rakhi made plans for a business trip to Bombay. She was anxious also to make a personal trip home to New Delhi to see her parents, who had not accepted proposals that they visit Nairobi.

Scott asked Rakhi, "Should I come with you to New Delhi?"

Considering, Rakhi replied, "I think it better I meet my parents first and smooth the way for you. It is possible you could join me at the end of my brief visit."

"Okay, but I don't like you travelling alone."

"All will be fine," she assured him with a kiss. "India is my home."

Chapter Thirteen

Abduction

The morning of her scheduled departure for Bombay, Rakhi took the hotel elevator to the lobby and crossed it to what she expected would be her waiting office car. As she exited the hotel's doors, two burly African men suddenly moved next to her, and she could feel a sharp point in her lower back. A knife, she knew. In a gruff voice, one of the men said instantly in a low firm voice directed to her ears alone, "Don't make a sound. You are coming with us." They pushed her into a taxi and sped off. No one was the wiser at the hotel entrance, least of all hotel security.

The men immediately pulled a hood over her head and injected her upper arm with a sharp needle. Rakhi was out in seconds.

Rakhi slowly regained consciousness. She could see that she was in a cinderblock room on a narrow mattress tossed on a larger heavy bed with an iron frame, to which she was handcuffed. There was no other furnishing in the rough room that had a wooden plank floor and similar ceiling. It seemed an unfinished structure. Then she became aware that there was a woman seated in the corner behind her. The woman said sharply, "Keep quiet!" She added harshly, "You will not be harmed if you don't resist."

At first, panic arose in Rakhi, an almost overwhelming tenseness that first spread heat through her body but then dissolved quickly. Her head ached.

"What is going on? Why have you taken me? Who am I to you?"

"Shut up. If you need to take a piss, I will guide you to a bucket in the corner. Otherwise, you need to know nothing."

Mid-morning in his office, Scott found another anonymous letter, unstamped. In typed letters, it said, "We have your wife. Do exactly what we say, and she will not be hurt. Await further instructions. Say nothing."

Scott groaned and vomited on the floor. In the other office, Bob rushed over. Scott gestured to the letter.

Bob put his hand on Scott's shoulder and waited a moment for his friend to regain some composure. Then Bob said, "My instinct is to take this to the police. But it is possible we are being watched and we should wait."

"Agreed." Then Scott thought and said, "Maybe the police are part of this. Maybe our phone is being tapped too. We're trapped."

Bob, thinking aloud, said, "Maybe I can go to the U.S. embassy and ask them for assistance. And let's telex the head office in New York. Our telex maybe won't be monitored."

"Why would anyone want to harm Rakhi?" Scott cried out, eyes tearing. "I'm the one writing provocative dispatches."

"Don't know. Let me call a friend to come to the office. You stay here." Bob picked up the phone and in a few minutes a friend from a rival news organization was in the office. A telex went to New York.

Bob planned to depart for the U.S. Embassy. When he opened the office door, he stepped on a folded paper. On the same typewriter was this note: **"Provide $100,000 for wife in small bills." "Further instructions coming."**

Bob took the new letter and left for the embassy. Scott paced. His journalist colleague tried to calm Scott with chatter. "Money can be found, can't it? This is not a large demand." Scott's mind raced. He could not be cooped up here, paralyzed.

"Let's go to your office. I want to call Rakhi's parents in India but am afraid to do so from here."

Within fifteen minutes, Scott had Mr. Seshadri on the line. Showing his military background, Mr. Seshadri had his emotions under control immediately. He had the funds. They could be wired from Delhi to Nairobi, likely through London and by using Standard Chartered, Rakhi's bank.

Old man Seshadri knew there were export controls on currency, but he didn't refer to them. He said also, "I will be in Nairobi tomorrow. Don't go to the police. They can't be trusted." And that was it. Nothing personal. All business, as if this was but yet another military maneuver from his days in the Indian Army.

The consular chief from the embassy called Scott to his office. There were others in the embassy meeting, which was held in a secure room. The Ambassador attended the meeting, which was chaired by another senior officer. He said Washington was involved. The Kenyan government needed to be informed. Kenya was a country friendly to the United States and could be counted on to provide assistance. Question was what was to done in the meantime. Washington did not authorize negotiation with criminals for release of abducted American citizens. At this moment, there was no way of knowing who was involved. No choice but to await a further communication from the abductors. The embassy did not think police were involved, but there was no explaining what Scott thought had been surveillance of his movements, starting in Mombasa some months earlier.

Scott reported that his father-in-law was gathering the funds and would be arriving in Nairobi tomorrow. Scott also related the other threatening notes sent to him, with the clear warning that he was to stop his reporting of police brutality of those in custody. Those senior in the room speculated that Scott was the real target and that Rakhi was easy leverage to get him out of the country.

"The old man coming from New Delhi could be a problem. We won't have much influence over him. Do you think he will go the Indian High Commission?" asked one of the senior officers.

"No, I think he believes he can handle this on his own," replied Scott. "I doubt he trusts anyone."

Someone else added, "Apparently the money is not a major obstacle for him."

Scott said, "No, I don't think it is. I don't think he will engage in any negotiation to try to reduce the demand, either. He is a man used to being obeyed and sees everything in black and white." He was growing impatient with the talk that contained no action plan.

Rakhi could see from a small window near the top of the wall of her bedroom cell that dusk was falling. She could occasionally hear the clucking of chickens. She must be in the countryside, maybe on a farm.

"I need to move my legs. Let me stretch. And I need to use that bucket." Rakhi said to her female captor.

Her handcuffs were unlocked. Rakhi sat up. Her female captor was a middle-aged, heavy-set African woman who looked every bit a no-nonsense character.

"Also, do I get something to eat? I'm not much use to you if I die of starvation. And why am I being held? What value do I have? The bank I work for isn't going to pay any ransom, if that is your expectation."

"Who cares what you think? Use the bucket and get back here to the bed. You'll be fed." Rakhi's keeper was curt and cold.

"So, who are you? Who do you represent?" demanded Rakhi.

"That is no concern to you. No talk." The woman knocked on the door, which was opened, and she departed. Later she returned with some dal and rice. "Eat."

Chapter Fourteen

Uhuru Park, Nairobi

Mr. Seshadri arrived on the afternoon flight from New Delhi, the same one Rakhi had taken six months earlier. Scott, Bob, and an officer of the U.S. Embassy were there to meet him. Seshadri's posture was straight as an arrow. With his trademark black suit and white shirt, his piercing grey eyes, and clipped military mustache, he commanded respect and authority. His greeting to Scott was formal and cold.

After entering the embassy car, Seshadri said, "Gentlemen, we are going to your embassy?" Answering his own question, he stated, "Good. We will talk there to establish our plan."

"Have you contacted your high commission?" asked the American embassy officer.

"No. Don't get overlapping authorities involved," advised Seshadri. He was taking charge of the situation, not the embassy, the police, Washington, or the local government. No one questioned him or his authority as they rode in silence to the U.S. Embassy in the middle of the city.

Once again in the secure room within the embassy, the working group convened. It included a ranking police official. The Ambassador shook Seshadri's hand and expressed his condolences that his daughter was involved in such a messy affair. Seshadri brushed aside the Ambassador's words. "We will get her back as long as no one does anything foolish," he replied.

Going on, Seshadri asked if there had been any further communique from the kidnappers. A random thought flashed through Scott's mind: *What was his father-in-law's rank in the army during his active days? He acts like a man accustomed to command and being obeyed without question.*

There had been another note overnight. It instructed the ransom cash be placed in a briefcase and left under a specific bench near the lake in Uhuru Park, which was on the edge of the city center. Five P.M. sharp. There was a further demand: Scott had to depart the country.

Seshadri asked for a phone to call the Standard Chartered Bank. One was provided. He confirmed that the funds he had arranged from New Delhi were in fact available and would be ready in cash within an hour. Hard currency regulations had been waived. Seshadri said he would pick up the funds forthwith. The others around the table, including the Ambassador, raised an eyebrow or two at his curt attitude, but Seshadri was in charge.

"Is there any way of communicating with the abductors?"

"No. They just say compliance is mandatory and Miss Seshadri will be released once the money is in hand. I assume now there must be some gesture that Scott is being sent from the country," came the reply from another senior official at the table.

The Ambassador added, "Mr. Seshadri, the U.S. government does not condone cooperating with terrorists and paying ransoms."

"And furthermore," the Ambassador went on, "Your daughter is not an American citizen and we have no legal responsibility for her. We are assisting because your son-in-law, an American, is threatened." Then, thinking perhaps this speech sounded too hard-hearted, he concluded, "But we are willing to assist with your daughter however we can."

Seshadri gave him a withering look, as if the ranking official in the room were an errant army conscript. "Thank you; I understand your official constraints."

Seshadri added, "You should understand the money is of no consequence. We can't communicate with these people, deliberately so it seems. We have no choice but to meet all their demands. And I will take the case with the currency to the park."

Looking at Scott, Seshadri said pointblank: "You better be packing your bags. I will leave a handwritten note in the bag saying you are leaving the country forthwith."

Scott had a momentary flash of anger at Seshadri's imperial behavior.

But Scott had no alternative to suggest. His home office had already given him an extended leave of absence.

"All right. Let's get moving. No reason for any police or embassy personnel to be in the area and spook the abductors. I can handle it. I will leave the bag and depart." With that, he got up, unofficially drawing the meeting to a close. "I need to get to the bank. Is there a car I can use?"

With a brief handshake to the Ambassador, Seshadri made his way to the conference room door. It was as though he was in his own office. An embassy officer escorted Seshadri to the entrance, where a nondescript embassy car was already waiting. Scott was left standing, as though he was of no consequence. Indeed, at this moment, he was not.

A few minutes before 5 p.m., Seshadri strove with purpose into the park and found the bench near the artificial lake. He put the bag under the bench, straightened, and walked away. Almost simultaneously, a terrific explosion blasted through the early evening air, sending a shockwave that knocked many park goers off their feet. Seshadri staggered but remained standing, in the best of the Indian Army tradition of how a brigadier should comport himself.

Of course, distract the police and the rest of us, he thought with satisfaction and a bit of admiration for the abductors. He assumed the bag was already snatched from the bench. He was right.

Seshadri found the embassy car on the edge of the park. He returned to the U.S. embassy as previously arranged. The working group reconvened and waited. Preliminary reports on television indicated that the bomb had been large but had been detonated in an open space, not damaging property nor harming individuals. Newscasters were speculating that it had to be the work of miscreants opposed to the government, but the lack of a specific target was puzzling. And, no group or individual stepped forward to claim responsibility.

Seshadri of course did not know what the motive of the terrorists might be, but he could see a method in their actions. They had kidnapped his daughter to put pressure on Scott's home office to withdraw him. There was nothing personal against his daughter. Seshadri admired the tactics. He was reasonably confident his daughter would be released unharmed, provided that local authorities did not try to grandstand.

They had no alternative but to await further communication about Rakhi. The group waited until midnight. Then a call came from the Intercon Hotel.

That evening, Rakhi demanded to be able to wash her face and brush her teeth. Her female guard gave her a basin and a toothbrush. Rakhi's emotional state was stable, tough, and clear-thinking. She was without question her father's daughter.

"What's your plan? Clearly it does little good to keep me here day after day."

"Don't talk so much. All will be clear soon."

"Why are you doing this?" Rakhi implored, in no way indicating distress in her tone, just a direct question requiring an answer.

"It is not for you to know."

Rakhi could tell it was not worth her effort to question a mere guard/babysitter. She also knew instinctively it was better to try to establish some kind of rapport with her captor.

"It must be pretty boring to sit here with me. What would you be doing otherwise?"

The heavyset lady, no fool herself, saw through Rakhi's little attempt to establish rapport. She ignored Rakhi.

Later at night, and Rakhi had no way of knowing the time because her watch had been taken from her, someone opened the door and passed a black piece of cloth to the female guard. She moved over to Rakhi and wrapped it around her head, blinding her. The lady guard took the handcuffs from the iron bed frame and refastened Rakhi's hands behind her back.

"Don't resist, scream, or do anything foolish. You will be hurt if you do. Just do what you are told."

Several rough hands held her firmly and led her outside to a car and pushed her into the back seat. A blanket was placed over her. The female guard squeezed in next to her.

Chapter Fifteen

Release and Departure

The car drove for perhaps a half hour, to Rakhi's mind. She could tell the driver was going along carefully, not speeding or careening. Clearly, he did not want to attract attention. The car came to a stop. The lady opened her door and grabbed Rakhi firmly. Another man joined her from the front seat and within seconds Rakhi was dumped on a concrete surface. They slammed the doors of their car and were gone. Rakhi for a moment was alone.

She struggled to her feet, but she could not see and could not reach up because of the cuffs to remove the blindfold. She was helpless but could walk. She heard traffic close at hand, so she stood motionless for a moment. Then there were men around her.

They removed her blindfold and spoke in friendly tones. Rakhi could see that she was on the street near the Intercon Hotel, from where she had been abducted two days previously. Police arrived. They knew who she was.

"Are you all right? Not hurt?'

"No. How do you know my name?"

The police official answered her gently. "We all know about you, Miss Seshadri. We have been working for your release," he added disingenuously.

"Where is my husband? I want him."

"He is on his way."

The police led Rakhi into the deserted hotel lobby, a place Rakhi knew well. Too well, perhaps. A police technician worked on her handcuffs and cut them off.

"I need to use a restroom," Rakhi said matter-of-factly. She was escorted to a hotel facility across the lobby. There were almost no patrons in the lobby to witness her first moments of freedom. Inside, Rakhi gratefully used a real toilet and washed her face. She tried with little success to brush her long black hair with her hands so that it was not in her eyes.

When she emerged, Scott walked in the door, along with her father. Rakhi and Scott embraced, and then father and daughter.

"You are now safe," said Mr. Seshadri. Scott was a little chagrinned that it was not he who got to say that to his wife. Nonetheless, it was the old man who had paid for Rakhi's freedom and organized the passage of money.

"Let's get upstairs," said Scott. The Kenyan police shook Rakhi's hand and departed, except for a contingent posted both in the lobby and in the hallway outside the rooms. The embassy contingent departed also. As much as Rakhi wanted to know the details of what had happened, she was overcome with fatigue and needed to sleep. They entered the elevator with Rakhi holding her father's hand. The three went to the same floor. The hotel had arranged a room for Mr. Seshadri next to that of his daughter and son-in-law.

At the door to their adjoining rooms, the old man said to Rakhi and her husband. "Rakhi is coming home to India for a while to rest." Then with a brief ceremonial hug for his daughter, he opened his door. Rakhi nodded and turned with Scott into their room. It was the first Scott heard that his wife was going home.

Rakhi headed for the shower. Over her shoulder, she asked Scott to order something from room service. It turned out to be unnecessary; the hotel had provided an enormous spread of fruits, crackers and cheese, cold cuts, and desserts. There also were flowers everywhere. Hotel management knew what it was doing in welcoming a special guest that night.

Rakhi emerged from the shower. Scott turned off the television, where news of Rakhi's release was playing. They embraced. Rakhi asked simply, "Why? Was it a kidnapping for money?"

"No, I don't think so. Somebody wants me out of the country for good, and they got their wish. The New York office has given me an extended leave. You were a pawn, I believe. I'm so very sorry. You weren't mistreated?" She shook her head.

Tears welled in Rakhi's eyes. She felt great empathy for her husband at that moment, more so than at any time in their relationship back to the days they walked together in the evenings in New Delhi.

She took his hand and looked him in the eyes, "Well, I did say I wanted adventure when I ran away with you. It's been a good ride so far."

Becoming serious, she said, "I have to go home for a while with my father. You know he won't be denied, and I want to be home and with my mother too." Scott nodded.

They fell asleep in each other's arms.

The next morning, Rakhi had to endure a series of debriefings with the Kenyan police, and she had a brief meeting with the American Ambassador. She also accepted a car from the embassy to the Kenyan Ministry of Foreign Affairs, where the Foreign Minister apologized for the misguided attitudes of some individuals in his country. He pledged the culprits would be found. Rakhi said thank you, and she, with her husband and father, departed for the airport. Realizing a mistake, she asked the driver to divert to her bank office. She thanked her superiors for brushing aside currency rules to allow the transfer of funds for her release. With affection, the bank manager wished her a good rest in India. He assured her that her future with the bank was secure. With that, Rakhi, the ambassador of goodwill supreme, finally departed for the airport.

The VIP lounge was waiting for her. She and her father did not need to go through customs. She had only hand luggage, in which were a few clothes she had selected from the hotel closet at the last minute.

An hour later, the flight to New Delhi boarded. Scott embraced Rakhi. She whispered in his ear, "I love you," and departed with her father. Scott stood quietly for a few seconds, then turned to find the embassy car. He returned to the empty hotel room.

Chapter Sixteen

New Delhi Return

Scott's office made it clear the next day that he needed to depart Kenya immediately. The head office gave him two months of personal leave and told him a good alternative to Nairobi would be worked out as an onward assignment. Scott decided to go to Bangkok, principally because it was not far from India and had no visa requirement. He knew he was not welcome at Rakhi's home in New Delhi at the moment. As for an ongoing assignment, Scott said thank you and asked to ponder at some future point what the assignment options might be. He shook hands with Bob and the office staff, asked Bob to sell his old range rover, and headed to the airport to depart for Thailand, exactly twenty-four hours after Rakhi had departed for New Delhi. It was not a twenty-four hours he wanted to remember.

Scott loitered in Bangkok for ten days awaiting his Indian tourist visa. He hardly left his room at the Oriental. He ordered room service and swam laps at the hotel pool. Many laps, several times a day. It was the most empty, worthless ten days of his life. He talked with Rakhi daily. She reported their separation was a needed time to allow her to patch things up with her parents, especially with her mother. Rakhi had not known that her mother spent two weeks in bed after the couple's abrupt departure from New Delhi six months back. There had been no question that she could have attended Rakhi's marriage ceremony in Arlington.

After ten days, Scott called Rakhi and said he was coming to New Delhi and had secured a room for the two of them at the Asoka Hotel, within walking distance of her parent's home and his old neighborhood. She said okay, not wishing to press her parents that she and Scott could stay together under their roof. In her parents' eyes, the two of them were not legally married.

Scott flew to New Delhi and checked into the Asoka, one of the older luxury hotels in New Delhi. It paled in comparison with the Oriental in Bangkok, but that was immaterial to Scott. He was sick inside. He wanted his wife, but he could not be certain of her affection, and whether they had a future.

From the Asoka, Scott took the five-minute taxi ride over to Malcha Marg. Rakhi's mother received Scott pleasantly; she was a lady and an affectionate one, but at heart her daughter's welfare was all that mattered to her. Rakhi's father was not at home. Scott recounted for both how heroic Mr. Seshadri had acted in Nairobi, taking control of the situation from both Kenyan and American officials. Scott pointed out that because Rakhi was not a U.S. citizen, the embassy's efforts on her behalf were extraordinary.

Rakhi's mother asked, "Was anyone held accountable for the abduction and the threats against you?"

Scott retold reports he had received that a few suspects were in custody. He had no idea, nor did his reporter friends in Nairobi, whether those in custody were correctly identified. In Scott's experience reporting police actions and brutality, he doubted whether the real culprits would be found, nor would it be discovered what the motive had been, except the obvious and successful one to get him out of the country.

Mrs. Seshadri's mother winced to hear again that her daughter had been threatened merely for her association with Scott. To herself, she rued the day Rakhi had met Scott, although she also believed he loved Rakhi and would always try his best to provide for her.

Scott returned to the hotel, not knowing his marital future.

Two hours later, Rakhi appeared at his hotel room.

"I'm staying with you, now and in the future. You and I belong together. We are married. My mother knows I am here and approves."

"Oh, God, thank you."

"I said in the beginning I wanted adventure and to see the larger world with you. I still believe in you and want to do that. But don't get me kidnapped again, and never lead me down dirt paths that end with water buffalo!"

Part III

LONDON: RAKHI'S STORY

Chapter One

Plotting Fun

Rakhi and Scott spent ten pleasant days together staying at the Asoka Hotel in New Delhi getting to know each other again after the trauma of the Nairobi kidnapping and Rakhi's return to New Delhi with her father. They made love again, somewhat hesitantly at first. More often, Rakhi held Scott in her arms and reveled in feeling safe with a man she knew would be by her side regardless of the challenges in their relationship.

Rakhi also was more comfortable with Scott because her parents were coming to terms with her marriage. It had been a crushing blow to Rakhi's mother to have her only daughter run away with an American to Kenya, get married in Virginia, and start married life in Kenya, a foreign land. Now Rakhi had voluntarily returned to India with her father after he had arranged her release from her abductors. Scott had shown his devotion by coming to her as quickly as he could. Her parents were getting used to the idea that Rakhi and Scott really were in love and were married, even if only in a civil ceremony.

As an indication of how far Rakhi's parents had accepted their daughter's marital status, the Seshadris invited their daughter and Scott out to dinner one night. Rakhi could not recall her parents ever dining at a restaurant, given their dietary restrictions imposed by their high caste status. Nonetheless, the Seshadris chose to take Rakhi and Scott to a good Chinese restaurant in the city center of New Delhi. The mood was cordial, and the vegetarian food was superb, even to the demanding standards of Rakhi's mother.

Returning from dinner, Rakhi sensed that a corner had been turned with her parents, and she expressed her relief to Scott later that night with an exceptional tenderness that he had not previously encountered from her. Later, they laid in each other's arms and talked of the future.

"I want to have a proper honeymoon," Rakhi began, stroking Scott's bare chest tenderly with her fingers.

"What would you like to do on this proper honeymoon?"

"You know what I want to do every morning and every evening. I want you in my arms, kissing me, and telling me how much you love me." Going on, she added, "And I want to wake up in a romantic city."

Warming to this topic, Scott suggested, "Let's go to Paris! That is a city I know well and want to share with you. We can linger over hot chocolate and croissants in bed, then wander streets fascinating no matter in which direction one walks."

"Oh, that would be wonderful" replied Rakhi enthusiastically. "And we would be safe!"

"Yes, my dear, we would be utterly safe, and Parisians love those in love," Scott added, hoping that this romantic sentiment would prove true. He vowed to make it so.

Thus, they decided a honeymoon had to be imminent. To herself, Rakhi recalled their less than happy first day of marriage, when after the morning ceremony in an Arlington Virginia law office they had gotten more than a bit drunk at a Georgetown pub and then had flown off to Florida the next morning to meet Scott's parents. To himself, Scott vowed he would always treat Rakhi like the princess she was to him.

In a burst of love and overflowing tenderness, Scott gathered Rakhi even more tightly in his arms and murmured, "Darling, I love you so."

"In fact," he added with heartfelt passion. "We must invent a word of endearment more potent, more meaningful, than darling."

"Please take your time, my sweetheart, and kiss me everywhere while you think of it ..."

Chapter Two

A Delayed Parisian Honeymoon

After making airline reservations, securing Rakhi's French visa, and choosing a hotel, an easy matter because Scott wanted nothing but the best for his lovely wife, the couple told Rakhi's parents they were heading off to Paris for a honeymoon.

Ever practical, Mr. Seshadri asked sternly why they had to go so far away. Rakhi revealed what even Scott did not know: She had been offered a position in the London headquarters of Standard Chartered bank. Her starting date was indeterminate and could easily accommodate a vacation. Mr. Seshadri nodded with approval. He was proud that his daughter was rising fast in her banking profession, and the old man grudgingly acknowledged to himself that Scott had made it possible by giving her a chance to move beyond the bank's New Delhi branch.

In a generous gesture, Mr. Seshadri offered the couple $20,000 as a wedding gift. Showing rare humor when Rakhi gasped at such news, Mr. Seshadri observed dryly that because his daughter had run off with a foreigner, he did not have to pay a hefty dowry to unload his daughter. Even Mrs. Seshadri smiled at that, not betraying her uneasy thoughts about how her daughter would balance a London banking career with children, which in her mind needed to happen soon.

Scott shook his father-in-law's hand, a gesture he had not done since first meeting him on the neighborhood street where he had engineered an encounter between himself and Seshadri with his daughter on a later afternoon stroll. Scott did not reveal what else was in his mind: If Rakhi was to work at Standard Chartered Bank in its London office, what was he to do to earn a living? His New York newspaper office had not suggested any onward assignment after the drama as a result of his Nairobi work and his hasty departure from Kenya demanded by Rakhi's captors. A follow-on London posting seemed a very remote likelihood. Scott pushed that thought to the back of his mind, preferring to think of how he and Rakhi would spend their days and nights in Paris.

Rakhi discovered that Scott was a very resourceful husband. He had arranged to have a limousine awaiting their arrival at Paris's Charles de Galle airport.

"Where are you taking me?" Rakhi asked, remembering that she had asked that very question of Scott when she first arrived in Nairobi and he had met her at the airport.

Picking up on that memory, Scott used the same words he had said on that earlier occasion, "To a place you will not soon forget."

The limo pulled under the canopy of the Plaza Athénée Hotel on the leafy Avenue Montaigne, surely the most exquisite of avenues in the world. The doorman opened Rakhi's door. Another employee opened the door of the hotel, giving Rakhi, stunning even after a long flight from New Delhi, an approving smile. *Ah*, he thought, *a beauty befitting this splendid hotel; indeed, a beauty among even those storied women who crossed his threshold daily.* Scott followed, knowing how John Kennedy must have felt when he said, even as President, that he was the fellow who accompanied Jackie to Paris.

Rakhi found a spray of three dozen red roses in their chamber, an opulent room overlooking the street of haute couture outside their window. *How does he arrange all these extravagances?* She wondered as she turned to Scott in utter gratitude. Reading her mind, Scott smiled with eyes twinkling, "I have a good friend at American Express." Rakhi retired to the marble and gold bathroom to luxuriate in a hot bath, which Scott joined. Thereafter they fell into the fabulous soft bed to sleep away the long international flight.

They were roused by mid-afternoon room service, which included a bottle of Dom Perignon on ice. More than tipsy, they later emerged from the hotel. Rakhi gazed with wonder that before her were the fashion houses of Dior, Louis Vuitton, Chanel, Prada. They happened immediately upon a lingerie shop. Scott, inspired by the sheer beauty of the silks, purchased Rakhi a flowing silk robe with skimpy sweet nothings underneath. The sales lady, a woman of great charm, Scott noted with appreciation, told them, "You have discriminating taste. You have chosen the champagne of silks." Rakhi suspected the purchase was greater in value than the airline ticket from India to France. Scott arranged for the package to be delivered to their room at the hotel, and the two lovers continued their stroll as the evening gathered around them.

They strolled in the direction of the Champs Elysees, that stupendous avenue connecting the Arc de Triomphe to the Place de la Concorde, two kilometers distant. The evening traffic on the avenue was heavy at that hour, but nothing could detract from the beauty and grandeur of the view. They sat on a bench among trees and said nothing, just absorbing the urban atmosphere. They were tired but happy together. Although it was still early evening, they turned back down the Avenue Montaigne to find their hotel.

Scott awoke rather early the next morning. He gazed at the sleeping beauty beside him. She had a slight smile. *How can one smile while asleep?* he thought. His second thought was *I am the luckiest fellow alive.* Scott gingerly climbed from the bed, ever so careful not to disturb Rakhi, and tiptoed to the bathroom, shutting the door quietly. He had an assignment for the concierge. Speaking quietly into the phone, he first ordered hot chocolate, croissants, and fresh strawberries. Then, he asked the concierge if he knew of a lady's apparel shop on the Boulevard St. Germain known for allowing women to try on high fashion clothes right in the aisle.

"Mais oui, monsieur, do you wish to use a hotel car so that the shop is easy to find?"

"Yes, si vous plait. Perhaps 10 o'clock?"

"Ca m'a fait plaisir, monsieur."

Scott showered briefly, and still with damp hair, climbed back in bed and feigned surprise when the hot chocolate arrived. The hotel had added a few roses in a vase. *It this place perfect?* wondered Scott. Rakhi remembered he had promised her hot chocolate in bed.

"This hotel is perfect!" she exclaimed with delight. "No, you are perfect," she corrected.

Before leaving the room for a day of adventure, Scott called the concierge again. "Please make luncheon reservations for two at La Closerie des Lilas."

"Good choice, Monsieur, and it is close to the ladies apparel shop."

Scott and Rakhi rode down the Boulevard St. Germain, across the river to the left bank but not too far from the hotel. Scott told Rakhi he was taking her on a cultural expedition probably unique to Paris. He did not say why it was unique except that the shop had exquisite high fashion clothes for women at very reasonable prices.

"That sounds fun, but don't be offended if I do not purchase a little black sleeveless dress with a short skirt. That is not for me."

Scott was not surprised, but to tease her, he asked why not.

"It is not my culture to show off one's legs in public, and I cannot do it."

"Don't worry. We'll visit this shop for a cultural experience only."

Rakhi gave him a puzzled look. The car stopped in front of a nice but ordinary shop along the boulevard in Montparnasse. Scott let the driver go, saying they could walk to the restaurant after the shopping. They entered. The shop was deep and narrow. It did indeed have high fashion clothing, and there were a few quite classy women examining the blouses and dresses. As they moved deeper into the store, Rakhi stopped with a gasp.

In front of her was an attractive, mid-thirties woman taking off her blouse to try on a store's selection. She was not wearing anything under her blouse. Then Rakhi saw another woman, equally attractive, taking off her skirt to try on one she had pulled from the rack. Rakhi did her best to appear nonplussed—that is, to seem as though such behavior was of course commonplace. She saw a few other women disrobing to sample merchandise.

Rakhi smiled and winked at Scott. "You devil! This is the cultural experience you wanted me to see?"

Scott was suddenly ashamed of himself. He was more abashed than Rakhi, who was clearly amused. "But I don't think this is the store for me," she said gently, taking his arm and moving in the direction of the entrance.

"Mais, madame, there is nothing you find of interest?" the saleslady asked, clearly meaning the fine selections on the rack.

"I'm afraid there is nothing here for me." The saleslady looked approvingly at Rakhi's fine silk sari and agreed perhaps another shop would be more appropriate.

On the sidewalk, Rakhi burst out laughing. "I guess I do not know you as well as I think I do! Clearly, I must watch my husband closely from now on."

Scott, even more sheepish, managed only a faint smile as they strolled down the boulevard. Finally, he said, "Well, Paris is not New Delhi, is it?"

Scott was relieved to find La Closerie des Lilacs. It was charming and relaxing. Diners could elect to eat outside, and most were doing so on this pleasant day. The outside dining area was enclosed by thick hedges that shielded the dining area from the noise of the street beyond. The headwaiter sat Scott and Rakhi next to a much older couple, she with an elegant green silk dress, pearls, and a little Pekinese dog at her feet. Her companion, much older, had an expensive blue blazer and French cuffs on his dress shirt; he looked exactly what he was, a retired high-priced attorney. Scott ordered white wine and onion soup, settling in for a long luncheon.

"I picked this spot not just because of its charm; it has been famous for well over a century for its literary patrons. For example, this is where Hemingway came in the mornings to write his short stories when he and his wife Hadley lived nearby and had almost no money for food. The waiters allowed him to sit all morning and write, with nothing more than one order of café crème."

"You know a lot about Hemingway," observed Rakhi.

"Well, I have read all he has written, or at least all that has been published. Took me years, and I have read most of the books about him too."

Going on, Scott related that it was in this restaurant in the mid-1920s that Hemingway showed F. Scott Fitzgerald what he was writing and sought his advice.

Scott noticed that the elderly couple next to him and Rakhi were giving them approving glances, even while they conversed constantly in French. The lady in green had a long story to relate. Because they were but inches from each other, Scott tried to listen to their conversation. His French was limited, but he tried to comprehend a bit. It turned out the other couple had limited English and were doing the same to Scott and Rakhi's conversation.

With an approving nod from Rakhi, Scott said hello to the couple, using his marginal French. They responded cheerfully; apparently glad the ice had been broken. Clearly, they were intrigued by this handsome couple of differing nationalities seated next to them. Pretty soon, Alain and Yvonne were exchanging biographic details with Rakhi and Scott. The French couple were decades-long friends, they said, with children from previous marriages. Scott immediately surmised the elegant blonde lady in green silk was the gentleman's mistress.

Scott deliberately ordered whatever courses Alain was ordering, through entrée to dessert, to cordials, to cheese, to coffee. The lunch lasted hours. Rakhi was as relaxed as was Scott.

Seeking a common topic, Scott mentioned a few French celebrities he admired, starting with Brigitte Bardot. Startled at the name, Yvonne volunteered that Alain and Brigitte had lived together when she was starting in films down on the Cote d'Azur. Alain smiled, admitting he and Brigitte had been close. Scott observed that Brigitte was single, as far as he could determine from the occasional magazine piece. Yes, allowed Alain, that was the case. Yvonne smiled indulgently at Alain. *What is it with this couple?* thought Scott.

Scott mentioned Juliette Greco, a French nightclub singer he had always loved. Alain and Yvonne knew of her too. They related that Juliette had had a passionate love affair in the late 1950s with Miles Davis, the American jazz trumpeter. They never married, though, because Miles did not want to live his life only in France, and he could not subject Juliette to the racist shunning she would face in the U.S. for marrying a black man.

"You know, you may be able to catch her singing at a nightclub in the Latin Quarter. She still performs once in a while," Alain told Scott.

When the meal was over, the two couples exchanged cards, except for Yvonne, who wrote her name, telephone number, and address on a napkin. Outside, the older couple got into a waiting car with a driver. Scott and Rakhi walked down the street, each realizing they had had a remarkable experience. They toured the nearby Luxembourg Gardens. Some of the beauty was lost on them, though, because they were sleepy after the long lunch and all the alcohol. They found a taxi and were at the hotel in twenty minutes, each happy to nap in the other's arms.

In the evening, they elected to stroll down the avenue to the right, instead of to the left as the previous night. The stroll this time took them in the direction of the Eiffel Tower, but they stayed on the right bank of the Seine, walking under the trees and enjoying the breeze along the river. And so ended their first full day of their honeymoon in Paris.

The next day, Scott brought back to the room a half dozen bottles of inexpensive champagne. Rakhi looked at him in alarm.

"What are you going to do with all that champagne?"

"We will drink it, my dear. But what I most want to do is pop the corks off the balcony." Taking a bottle, he opened it on the balcony after giving it a little shake. The cork exploded out of the bottle and sailed in an impressive trajectory before landing in the garden below. "That's how I want to celebrate our honeymoon!" Rakhi got into the spirit and shot off a cork also into the garden. Then they sipped the wine, kissed, and sipped some more. The hours slipped by.

After ten days of sipping, strolling, dining, sleeping, exploring, and kissing, they were sated. There was nothing they had not done in the City of Lights. Perhaps they knew each other a little better, perhaps not. At least they agreed they were ready for the next chapter in their life together, setting up housekeeping and learning how to work in London.

Chapter Three

First Days in London

Rakhi and Scott said goodbye to the Plaza Athénée, with a special thanks from Scott to the concierge, and headed via the cross-channel ferry to London. They had chosen a modest hotel near the Kensington Park end of Hyde Park. From there it would be a bit of a ride on the tube to get into the business area of the West End, but the two had an idea they would like to find some sort of living accommodation in Notting Hill, also in the general area near the park.

It was a shock for both of them to contemplate re-entering married life outside of their Parisian honeymoon bubble. Before turning out the light that first night in London, Rakhi turned to Scott and asked, "Will you come with me tomorrow morning when I report to the bank? At least come with me to the building?"

"Of course, my dear. I will do anything to support you, and at this moment, you are the sole breadwinner. After you are situated, I can search out the London office of my paper and tell them I am here, but who knows what that will accomplish?"

The next morning the two of them, fortified by a hearty British breakfast, collected tube and street maps and headed out to the local tube entrance. The crush of commuters was daunting after the quiet luxury of the famous Parisian hotel, but they made it into "the City," the financial area of London where Standard Chartered had its head office on Basinghall Avenue. Scott kissed Rakhi goodbye at the imposing building's entrance and squeezed her hand also for good luck. Rakhi took a deep breath, entered the building, waved back at Scott through the glass doors, and disappeared within the structure.

Scott turned and went to the London office of his New York-based newspaper. It was a fair distance from the financial district, but Scott enjoyed walking in the famous city that he did not know too well. Eventually he climbed to the third-floor cramped office, a far cry from the drama of the bank's impressive presentation. He introduced himself to the manager, Jones, who barely knew his name and little about his reporting in South Asia and East Africa. Jones said it was likely he would be hearing from the New York office about some type of work for Scott in London, but so far, Jones had no communication to pass along. With a perfunctory handshake, Jones dismissed Scott and said he would be in touch.

Meanwhile, Rakhi had a far more personally satisfying greeting at her bank. She had an appointment with a vice president named Williams, who knew the details of her work in New Delhi and in Nairobi. Williams said the bank looked forward to her joining their team. Williams accompanied her to a more senior officer's plush office, where he and his superior, Jenkins, planned to discuss the role they had in mind for Rakhi.

Jenkins, perfectly dressed in a fine grey pin-striped suit that Rakhi would in time recognize as typical of a bespoke one hand cut and stitched on Saville Row, waved Rakhi to a corner of his office where there were several overstuffed chairs and a coffee table with a Persian rug underneath it.

They settled in, and Jenkins asked how she had fared on her personal leave after the tumult in Nairobi.

"Well, sir," replied Rakhi with a kind smile, "my husband took me on a two-week honeymoon to Paris. We've only been married less than a year, and we went straight to Nairobi after getting married in the States."

"So, I am perfectly rested now and ready to join the working world again," she concluded.

Jenkins and Williams exchanged a look that suggested this young woman had the social grace to pull off what they had in mind for her.

"Good. You may be curious what responsibilities we have in mind for you at this office. This is it in a nutshell. Hear us out before you reply."

"A growing area within international banking is what you may have heard of as private banking—that is, the management of the assets of ultra-high net-worth individuals who entrust a significant portion of their investment portfolios to us to manage. We think with your educational background and work in two different countries for the bank, you could be a strong candidate for such a position."

Jenkins paused to garner her reaction. Rakhi replied with candor, "As you probably know, my bank responsibilities so far have been on the technical side of foreign currency exchanges and a bit in Kenya on convincing Asians not to abandon their investments in that country. I do not have experience in the management of investment assets. Why do you think I would be able to take on this new responsibility?"

Again, Jenkins thought to himself, this is a straight-talking young woman who can hold her own in serious business discussions. To Rakhi, he replied, "We can teach you the basics of investment portfolio management, but in most cases, experts back here will take care of that. What you must do is search out potential customers abroad and convince them they cannot live without our guidance, and in the first instance that guidance will be yours."

Rakhi considered a moment, "So this would be a sales job?"

"Yes, but a sales job in which millions are at stake with every client."

Jenkins expected an excited acceptance of his proposal. Rakhi, though, was thinking through the implications of this proposed assignment. What she said was, "There would be a great deal of travel involved."

"Yes, is that acceptable? We have fairly well ploughed the ground here in the U.K., but much needs to be done in the Persian Gulf, to say nothing of Japan and elsewhere in the Far East and South East Asia. You could explore prospects in India, too."

Rakhi thought it time to show some enthusiasm. "I would be pleased to try this type of assignment. Just so that we understand each other, though; I am recently wed and cannot spend all of my time separated from my husband."

Williams spoke up, "That we appreciate and can accommodate. You should know that the bank also is committed to bringing women into the ranks of middle and senior management here, and success in this proposed endeavor would be rewarded handsomely in increased responsibility."

Jenkins walked over to his desk to retrieve an envelope and folder for her. Returning to his seat, he handed Rakhi the envelope, saying, "Inside is a written offer of what we have been discussing, plus proposed compensation. Discuss it with your husband and let us know tomorrow what you think." Williams added that he would show her the office they had in mind for her, and she should report to him the following day.

Rakhi departed the plush office, in part flattered and more than a bit nervous that the expected travel would be a problem for her and Scott. She was impressed, though, that her proposed office was a private one and had an assigned lady who would be her assistant.

Scott spent the balance of his morning talking with real estate agents who could assist with the letting of a flat. He told one agent of his desire to find a flat in the West End, and he was dismissed as being impractical. Nothing in the immediate city could be leased at rates he could afford. The next agent listened to his proposal about finding something in Notting Hill. The agent pointed out that the area was not a very desirable location because of a history of ethnic rioting in the area and its heavy concentration of immigrants. In fact, the general area was sometimes referred to as a slum. Scott was told, on the other hand, the area was undergoing gentrification as some far-sighted investors were renovating old and dilapidated, but previously stylish, residences and dividing the interiors into small flats.

Scott and Rakhi reconvened for lunch at an Indian restaurant not too far from Harrod's department store. Scott was impressed with Rakhi's job offer, not thinking some international travel would be a problem. Rakhi read the formal job description given to her by Jenkins, and she thought the compensation was all right, although she and Scott had little clue what their living expenses would be. They met the real estate agent for a tour of the Notting Hill flat. It was on a lane that was a bit busy with fruit stalls and all manner of knickknack shops and the townhouses all were painted in bright pastels, but it was a place to call home. They signed a year's lease. They went to bed that night with some sense of accomplishment regarding the day's achievements, but in truth, Rakhi was uneasy about her travel prospects, and Scott was discouraged about his future employment.

Chapter Four

Rakhi's Introduction to the Bank

The next morning Rakhi arrived early to take possession of her new office at the bank and meet properly her assistant, Eunice, who asked her straightaway if she would like a cup of coffee. Shocked, Rakhi declined and said as nicely as she could, "Maybe there will be times when I will ask if you wish a cup of coffee, but on a regular basis, I hope you and I can be friends with no fetching of coffee or other errands. I know I won't be able to survive in this new office and new city without guidance, and I hope you can help me on that score." Eunice gave her a grateful smile that suggested sisterhood, to the extent possible within the first minutes of a new relationship. "I'll try my utmost to help you. This place can be complicated to figure out," gesturing to indicate she meant the immediate office.

Rakhi did ask Eunice to seek an appointment for her upstairs with Williams, her immediate superior. Within fifteen minutes, she was in Williams' office. She handed him the packet of completed employment forms she had been given the day before, and she placed on his desk the memo spelling out her job description and the salary terms. "Thanks for doing all this work so fast," he responded.

"I filled out the forms, and I am pleased to be starting here. There is one thing I am concerned about, though, and that is the salary. It does not seem too generous. I took possession of a flat yesterday afternoon, and my compensation won't be going too far after rent is paid. Is there some flexibility in that final number?"

Williams listened to her speech with a frown and replied, "Well, this is a bit irregular. I will look into the matter and get back to you."

Continuing, Williams, all business, said, "Let's now get to work. I assume you don't know much about personal investment matters—that is, stock exchanges and the difference between equity markets and debt markets." He had a condescending manner, especially when he lit a pipe, making a production of the ceremony and filling the room with smoke.

"No, not in detail. My bank responsibilities previously had to do with foreign currency exchanges and then in Kenya, the development of contacts in the Asian population there to convince them to keep their investments in Kenya."

Williams interjected, "And that latter work is why we have offered you this opportunity here in London. You will, as you ascertained yesterday, be a salesman for the bank's expertise in managing the personal investment portfolios of very rich individuals. We think a woman could be very helpful in this responsibility."

Continuing, Williams said, "You need to know the basics of financial markets to make your sales pitch convincing. So, I have arranged a two-week crash course in how financial markets operate and the diverse investment tools that are available to the clients you will be dealing with." He picked up a stack of books from the corner of his desk and gave them to Rakhi. "Read these. And you will have a tutor from our personal investment side for the next two weeks."

It was obvious to Rakhi that the brief meeting was drawing to a close. She looked Williams in the eye and asked evenly, "What did you mean by saying a woman could be very useful as a salesman for the bank?"

Williams surveyed her carefully and took the pipe from his lips. "Because you are attractive, that's why, and you will be dealing with wealthy and important men in various countries. They will not expect a woman in their offices, and you might be able to provide the edge that will get their attention." Adding as an afterthought, "You will need some advice on clothing. A sari is fine here in the office, but on business trips, you will need to have Western dresses and suits in your wardrobe."

Rakhi knew already she did not like Williams, and she did not appreciate the way he looked at her. She left his office with a sense of foreboding.

Rakhi returned to her office and found a young Pakistani named Naim waiting for her. "Welcome to the bank, Mrs. Higgins. I've been asked to give you a tutorial in financial markets." Thinking he should explain, he added, "I come from that division in the bank." Rakhi felt immediately at ease and insisted she was Rakhi. She thought to herself that she had not been called Mrs. Higgins since the day she had been married.

"Good. Let's start with the basics of market organization this afternoon and tomorrow we will pay a visit to the London financial exchange," Naim said enthusiastically.

She and Naim had hardly started when Eunice got a call inviting Rakhi upstairs to Jenkins' office. Rakhi remembered Jenkins was her superior's boss. She entered his tastefully decorated office with anticipation that her summons had to do with her requested salary boost. Jenkins ushered her to his seating area that had four comfortable chairs framed by a hand-woven Iranian carpet she recognized as a Tabriz similar to one her father owned. She complimented him on his fine taste in Tabriz carpets.

"Oh," he said kindly and thought to himself, *This lady is sophisticated.* "You know your carpets. I acquired this on a business trip to Tehran. Not many who come to this office notice the carpet, let alone know its style."

"But I didn't ask you here to discuss Oriental carpets. I heard from Williams that you are not pleased with the level of compensation we offered you."

Rakhi replied, "It isn't really displeasure. It is that my husband and I are strangers to this city and do not know what our living expenses will be. It was a shock yesterday to rent a flat and realize that it will take much of my month's earnings."

Jenkins looked at her with kind eyes and said, "I understand completely, and London is so much more expensive than New Delhi or Nairobi. And getting more expensive by the day."

Jenkins went on, "If we increased your annual salary by 20 percent, would that help put your mind at ease?"

Startled, Rakhi said that his response was generous, especially when she had hoped for 10 percent. She departed the office pleased by the extra boost to her salary. He was a man she thought she could speak frankly with and could trust. The passage of time would prove her instinct correct.

Chapter Five

Settling into London

The next two weeks for Rakhi had her engulfed during the day with instruction from Naim on financial markets, and at night with the study of materials he gave her. The Parisian honeymoon was already a distant memory. Scott spent his days arranging telephone service in the flat, buying curtains, renting basic furniture such as a bed, a couch and a kitchen table and even purchasing crockery, pots and pans and silverware for the kitchen. Thereafter, he had to find where one bought groceries and other household supplies, and he began to stock the little pantry, all the while constantly dipping into the remaining funds from Mr. Seshadri's cash wedding gift. He heard nothing from his press office, even after stopping by again to give them his telephone number and mailing address. For him too, the Parisian honeymoon was not only a distant memory, it was almost a painful one as he recalled how extravagant they had been with money.

It was two weeks before they had the time on a Saturday morning to stroll into nearby Kensington Park and enjoy the trees, the green gardens, and the flowers. It had also been almost two weeks since they had had the time to make love. They tried to make up for lost time that weekend.

One matter bothered her considerably. She did not know what the best way was to handle Jenkins' comment about her need to acquire a few Western clothes. Should she ignore him? Or conform to the dress code that offended her. She decided to consult her assistant, Eunice, who herself dressed well in conservative business attire.

Eunice proved to be completely practical. "Believe me, you will need every advantage you can muster to bring in new accounts. If it means showing a little leg, it's a small price to pay." The two of them went to Harrod's over a long lunch break. Rakhi came back with several black business suits and a little black dress, the very items with short skirts she vowed in Paris she would never wear.

Williams called her into his office on the very day she wore her business suit for the first time. He looked her up and down approvingly. "I see you are getting adjusted to London. It is timely that you have upgraded your wardrobe because we need to start planning your first business trip abroad." Going on, he asked, "Have you given any thought about your first market trip?"

Rakhi was taken aback. How could she be travelling abroad after only a few weeks in the office? She had not, in fact, given much thought about where she should travel. She had been engrossed with her studies. Williams answered his own question: We think you should go to the UAE, Dubai specifically. That is a boomtown, with a lot of money flowing there these days. That market deserves scrutiny." Concluding, he said, "Plan to go a week from today. In the meantime, get together with our Middle East specialists to develop an itinerary and a list of potential high rollers to meet." He dismissed Rakhi, noting as she left his office that she did indeed, just as he anticipated, have nice legs.

At home that night, Scott was by equal measure angered that Rakhi had to go off travelling so soon and impressed that she was jumping into her portfolio so fast. He realized immediately that Rakhi had a lot of work to do to get ready. He vowed not to distract her.

Chapter Six

Dubai

A week later, Rakhi descended the stairs from the British Airways flight from Heathrow to Dubai International Airport, a gleaming facility. The ferocious heat of the August day hit passengers who had to walk a short distance into the terminal. A car from the Metropolitan Hotel took her to that hotel, opened only two years previously in 1979. The structure with its gardens was truly an oasis amidst sand dunes on the edge of the city. En route to the hotel, all Rakhi could see were cranes constructing dozens of buildings simultaneously. The term "boomtown" did seem to define the city emerging from the desert.

Rakhi's first order of business was to check in with local Arab contacts developed from her London office. Rakhi confirmed the three appointments she had with members of the royal family. At each appointment, Rakhi's Arab hosts greeted her with extreme courtesy, but Rakhi learned that essentially the bulk of their financial assets were committed to the diverse development projects, ranging from commercial office buildings, to hotels, to retail shopping malls. Discouraged, Rakhi finished her meetings in one day and took a second day to tour the gold souk along the creek that divided the old town from the rising new city of existing and planned skyscrapers. Rakhi had the car stop so that she could watch the dhows being loaded for their impending sea voyage south to Mombasa and Zanzibar. She remembered fondly her visit to Mombasa with Scott and seeing the dhows enter the Mombasa port from the Persian Gulf.

On the morning of her third day in Dubai and some hours before her departure, Rakhi received an unexpected call at her hotel from the last of the three individuals she had met initially. She returned to his office. To her surprise, her Arab host asked her graciously to explain again what financial services Standard Chartered could offer to manage a portion of his personal funds. And specifically, what types of opportunities might be made available that would not be available to other investors? Rakhi went over again the range of personalized investment options, including advance notice of initial public offerings. On the spot, she received a promise of one million pounds sterling. Rakhi returned to her hotel elated by her good fortune. What had transpired over the course of two days since her initial meeting? She had not learned yet that it was considered bad form culturally to turn down flatly an overture from a prestigious British bank.

Rakhi reported this development to Williams in the London office and boarded her flight home. Scott met her with kisses in the evening after she made it back to their little Notting Hill flat. The next day in the office, Williams allowed that the bank considered her first venture abroad to be a fine success. He invited her to lunch to acknowledge her first account. Rakhi tried to decline, thinking a lunch to be out of proportion to her short trip with one new account. Still, Williams insisted and took Rakhi to the Brown's hotel restaurant, a location some distance from the financial district. Rakhi did not enjoy or appreciate Williams' attempt to engage in small talk, but she was sufficiently adept to keep the conversation from stalling. In the back seat of the taxi returning to the bank, Williams placed his hand on her knee.

Startled, she looked down at his hand that continued to linger on her knee, removed his hand firmly, and shifted away from him. She understood instantly the reason for the luncheon invitation. It had been an excuse to be with her alone and outside of the office. She said to him firmly, "Do not ever do that again." Williams said nothing. He was not deterred. In his experience, most women to whom he had made such overtures said the same thing initially.

Chapter Seven

Rakhi's Expanding Career and Troubles

In the several years that followed her initial foray to Dubai to find business for the bank among the super-rich, or "ultra-high net worth individuals" as they were becoming known in the world of private investment banking, Rakhi grew increasingly successful and well-paid. She expanded her search to include India, Pakistan, Singapore, and Japan.

She was a natural salesperson in India, principally the cities of Bombay and Calcutta, as she combined her clearly high social status (determined by her name and her accent), her sterling academic credentials, her growing expertise about the world of private banking, and her social polish, to say nothing of her stunning appearance and that she represented one of the world's important banking and investment houses. She had coldly calculated that even in India, as elsewhere in Asia, to wear Western business attire, coupled with some refined jewelry, was a signal to her clients that she represented international sophistication.

On her own, Rakhi found a smaller market also in Karachi, Pakistan, where there was a pocket of considerable wealth representing industrialists and large landowners anxious to find investment protection for their liquid assets outside of the country. Her superiors in London, including Jenkins, were greatly impressed with her skill to identify this smaller market and move to exploit it successfully.

Rakhi found Singapore to be the most lucrative garden to plough and thereafter to tend. Of the three ethnic groups there (Chinese, Indian, and Malay), roughly balanced in population in that island nation, the Chinese were just beginning to have the greater levels of liquid assets to invest, and they looked with favor on the services of a trusted British financial institution.

Rakhi had settled into a travel routine that kept her out of London several weeks of every month. When she was at home, she was swamped with work, much of which she had to take home at night.

Her husband, Scott, had considerable patience and an almost unlimited pride in his wife's business accomplishments. Still, eventually he resented her absence from home and her constant work brought home from the office. Her professional accomplishments also put his languishing career prospects in a poor light by comparison. His office had not provided him a proper reporting position that would allow him to follow major political events, of which there were many with the changes that the new prime minister, Margaret Thatcher, was implementing. Instead, the office asked him to do feature articles on tourism and to highlight the scenic wonders of England for American tourists to explore, such as Offa's Dyke separating England and Wales, or Hadrian's Wall separating England and Scotland. He hiked alone the length of both trails while Rakhi was abroad and produced highly readable accounts of his discoveries along the path. In Scott's mind, his current work, even if praised, was of no consequence compared to his reporting on an aircraft hijacking and a failed military mutiny in Bangladesh, or the burning of the U.S. Embassy in Pakistan. He looked back with frustration that he had been unearthing human rights abuses in Kenya. For that, he was rewarded by writing tourist stories?

Inevitably, Rakhi and Scott's lives diverged professionally, but they also suffered personally. They rarely had moments together for physical intimacy, and on the few occasions when Scott pressed Rakhi on the matter, she referenced what she saw as the legitimate constraints on her—that is, her travel requirements, and considerable fatigue when she was at home.

Rakhi did not mention to Scott that her life brought her into contact often with highly attractive men with unlimited funds to entertain her while abroad. Her office expected her to accept dinner invitations and to attend cultural programs if invited by her clients. Her job was to be ingratiating, but it was understood rather than stated policy that there were ethical boundaries she should not cross. That is, her behavior should not bring embarrassment to the bank, nor should she place herself in a compromising professional situation. Rakhi did neither as a matter of course, but her lifestyle while abroad did over time make her home life, such as it was, seem boring and Scott a little parochial.

At a deeper psychological level, Rakhi was becoming antagonistic to men. Perhaps it was a legacy of being the only daughter of an authoritarian father. Her college days facing Eve-teasing in India also planted in her some antipathy to men. The Eve-teasing at Miranda House College and Delhi University, both at the same campus, was usually far more vicious than the benign name suggested, and occasionally the never-ending practice was disturbing and frightening.

Now in her adult life in a so-called glamorous lifestyle, she could hardly keep from rolling her eyes in disgust when men made advances to her. Some of those advances were subtle, such as being overly charming at dinner in a cozy restaurant after several glasses of wine, and others were explicit, such as touching her, either casually or explicitly. The wealthier of her male clients occasionally invited her on weekends aboard their yachts. Rather than being enticed by these overtures, she was repulsed. One result of her apparently glamorous lifestyle was that, ironically, her sexual interests dwindled considerably as she saw the darker side of powerful and important men. Her husband, Scott, was an unwitting victim of her growing antipathy.

It did not help that Williams, now her superior of some years' standing, continued his advances to Rakhi. They took the form of an occasional suggestive remark, a frequent eyeing of her breasts rather than looking her in the eye, and a periodic luncheon invitation that she always declined.

One evening when Rakhi worked late and the office was deserted, she was surprised when he appeared at the door to her office. "Have you got a minute?" he asked.

"Of course. What is on your mind?"

"You are," he replied. "I want to take you out."

"Mr. Williams, you know that is not possible, nor will it ever be possible. We are just employees working in the same division. You are my supervisor at that."

"As your supervisor, I want to get to know you better. I don't know anything about your background, for example. I would like to hear about your college days."

"No, you don't," replied Rakhi impatiently. "You want to sleep with me. You need to leave this office right now."

"You are correct. I do want to be intimate with you. My wife and I have an open relationship. Neither cares what the other does. And it is only sex, not a life-time commitment."

"You leave now, or I call security." Rakhi stood up and reached for the phone. She did not immediately dial, however.

Williams figured that her not dialing meant she was pondering his offer, despite her words. He moved fast to put his hand firmly over hers, blocking Rakhi from lifting the receiver. Simultaneously, he moved around her desk so that he could grasp her from behind with his free arm. Then he removed his hand from the telephone so that he could pin her arms behind her in preparation for pushing her to the floor and pulling up her skirt. Instinctively, Rakhi jabbed Williams hard on the foot with the spiked heal of her shoe. He let go of her for a moment. She pushed herself free and fled from her office. She left the building without contacting security. She wanted to get far away fast.

That night, Rakhi chose not to tell Scott of the encounter. Sensing her unsettled state of mind, he made an amorous gesture, touching her arm not unlike what Williams had done some hours earlier. Rakhi pushed Scott away. "No, I don't want that. Leave me alone!"

The next morning, Rakhi was in Jenkins' office early. She related the events of the previous evening regarding Williams. Jenkins listened closely, not interrupting the flow of her words. When she was done, Jenkins said he would handle the matter, and he asked her to return to her office—or take the day off—but not say anything to Eunice or others about the incident. Rakhi chose to go to the British Museum alone and thereafter eat at a nearby Indian restaurant.

The next day, Eunice greeted her and said, "Mr. Jenkins wants to see you immediately."

Upstairs, Jenkins was as gracious as he could be, ushering her to his comfortable chairs on the Tabriz carpet. "Rakhi, the senior management regrets what happened the other night with Williams. After this meeting, I am to escort you upstairs to the Executive Suite so that an appropriate apology can be extended. Before I do, however, I wanted to get your views on a promotion we have in mind for you. We want you to take the position Williams had. He is gone, terminated for cause."

"Would you be comfortable with the promotion?" asked Jenkins kindly.

Rakhi was taken aback, both by the offer of a promotion, but also by the fact that Williams was out of her life. Her first reaction was visceral: "Will I be required to sit in his office?"

"Humm. I understand," was the reply from Jenkins. "No, we will find you an appropriate office on this floor near me."

"Will I be travelling as much as I did before? Williams did not."

"No, you will supervise your replacement, once someone is identified. And supervise others as well."

"I will be happy to take the promotion. But I want Eunice to come with me."

"No problem," was the reply from Jenkins. "She is good, no doubt. You have an eye for talent."

Concluding the meeting, Jenkins added, "Take off the day and tell your husband about the promotion. Then take him to a really nice place for lunch with the substantial earnings you will be getting with this promotion. See you tomorrow up here. A new office will be waiting."

Chapter Eight

Scott's Problems

Rakhi did not know where Scott was, so she could not immediately get in touch with him about the promotion. She took herself out once again for lunch, this time to her favorite Indian restaurant, Shezan, near Harrod's Department store.

Of course, Rakhi did not know that Scott was with another woman. He was with Nasreen, his Indian friend from years back. The lady who had taken him to the Playboy Club. Being lonesome when Rakhi was always abroad and sexually frustrated from months without a touch from her, Scott wanted a female friend. Nasreen was not hard to find. She still worked at the publishing house, she had remained single, and she still had the same apartment.

When he looked her up, Nasreen was as straight forward as he recalled, "Didn't you get sick of me that night at the club?"

"Yes, you were bad. But that weekend, the sex was good, really good. I recall you mixed gin and tonics at 11 in the morning and put on 'The Hustle.' I need your company, and we know each other."

"Fair enough. I need some company too."

They had been meeting for six months. It had been easy when Rakhi was gone two or more weeks at a time. Rakhi had been rejecting Scott sexually for quite some time, and Nasreen was a free spirit, ready at a moment's notice to entertain Scott, accept his pent-up desires, and share her needs. It was an arrangement of mutual convenience.

On the day of her promotion and at the lunch hour, Scott was with Nasreen at her place, drinking and doing the things each needed to have done to the other. That evening, Scott and Rakhi met up at their flat as though each had had a normal day. Rakhi had brought home Indian carryout, and she explained why she had been at an Indian restaurant for lunch instead of at the office. She told Scott she was celebrating a promotion. He was jubilant.

Rakhi hesitated to tell him of the sexual assault she had endured, but over sweet rice pudding for dessert, she told him the rest of the story regarding Williams.

"I did all I could in recent years to keep him at arm's length, but he finally forced himself on me. I would have been raped, Scott."

Scott took her in his arms to try to comfort her as she began to cry, then sob. He stroked her cheek gently.

"Just do that, please. I need comfort."

Scott held her well into the night until he could tell from her regular breathing that she had fallen asleep. He then extracted his numb arm being used as a pillow and curled up beside her. He loved her, but he hated himself.

Chapter Nine

A Double Life

For Rakhi and Scott, in the next several years life improved considerably in a material sense. Rakhi excelled in her management of those working under her supervision to develop the private banking division. She herself continued to travel occasionally to meet her most wealthy clients, those with the much larger accounts. Although she was not aware of it, senior management at the bank was grooming Rakhi for top responsibility. In the meantime, Rakhi's compensation had become significant, allowing her and Scott to purchase a larger house in the increasingly gentrified Notting Hill area. The house, like the others in the enclosure, opened onto a shared private garden available only to the residents of that little neighborhood.

Scott had finally been given a proper reporter's beat, covering domestic political matters within the U.K. He continued to see Nasreen. Each needed the other for sex, and as a few years passed, they became comfortable friends with an explicit bargain between them.

Rakhi's parents came to visit, an event quite surprising because both never wanted to travel abroad. Still, they arrived, and then saw no reason to leave the house. They had no interest in museums, the theater, or restaurants. Mr. Seshadri allowed that he had had enough of the British pre-partition to last him several lifetimes. The restaurants they had to endure, though, because Rakhi had not developed any culinary skills. Fortunately, there was a very good vegetarian restaurant in their neighborhood.

Rakhi's mother had become rather insistent that she wanted grandchildren. Rakhi told her it apparently wasn't God's plan that she become pregnant. The truth her mother did not know was that Rakhi and Scott had had so little sex in recent years that the odds were against her becoming pregnant now that she was approaching forty years of age.

In fact, Rakhi, despite her history for years of rejecting the entreaties from men, had in recent times developed a relationship with a Chinese man in Singapore, a gentleman so wealthy even he did not know how much money he had. His wealth came from commercial real estate development in mainland China and elsewhere in Southeast Asia. Rakhi and her team helped him get richer.

Rakhi could not explain to herself why she picked up with the Chinese gentleman, practically old enough to be her father. Was she looking for a father-figure? Or perhaps it was because he was affectionate and safe. Especially that he was safe. That is, he asked nothing of her. The private banking services he received from her team could have been found elsewhere. There were no cultural undertones. Nothing political to complicate matters. No falling in love. All the older gentleman wanted from Rakhi was sex, and more often than not considering his age, nothing more than physical closeness and a sensual massage he could give her. Rakhi obliged and reciprocated his gentle touches and massages.

It did not hurt that she could indulge any whim she wanted, including champagne baths and caviar for breakfast. That, however, was really superficial. More profoundly, Rakhi, like her husband, had made an explicit bargain to receive what mysterious physical and psychic needs she had that could not be provided by her spouse.

Their double lives continued for several years more. They had been married for ten years, and each pursued a professional career that was satisfying, while their marital life was a convenient arrangement. Rakhi and Scott were friends, but as the years passed, they did not have a sexual marriage at all. She told Scott it was his fevered imagination that all married couples were having sex. He didn't argue much about that, since he was being taken care of by Nasreen, and he had decided that if and when Nasreen was no longer available, he would find a replacement. Rakhi too was being taken care of. No one at the bank questioned why she continued to travel to Singapore. The fees her wealthy client earned the bank were enough to more than justify a trip out there every month and a hefty lodging bill from Raffles' hotel, although in fact Rakhi spent most of her nights in her gentleman friend's lavish villa.

Chapter Ten

Death

Rakhi's father died in his sleep. The call from New Delhi came at midnight from the long-time neighbor to the Seshadri residence. The neighbor, Mrs. Choudhury, told Rakhi that her mother was calm but in a mild state of shock because of the suddenness of the event. Rakhi spoke briefly to her mother, who told her the funeral service had to be in two days. Rakhi told her mother she and Scott would be home as quickly as possible.

After Rakhi put the phone down, she told Scott, standing next to her by the phone, the news and wept almost silently in his arms. He held her for fifteen minutes, not saying a thing.

"I'll make the flight reservations just now. I'll leave the return date open."

He turned to the phone and called British Airways straightaway. He made reservations for the mid-morning flight a day later, giving himself one day to get an Indian visa.

Rakhi nodded assent and stood indecisively for a moment. Then she brought out a suitcase and began packing it. She knew how to pack for long flights and was done within a half-hour. Scott tried to do the same but with less success.

"Don't you think you should come to bed for a few hours of sleep?" Scott asked.

"I guess so."

But the night was long and little sleep occurred. Rakhi went to her office after stopping at a store to buy a white sari. She knew it was expected of her as a daughter to wear white, as it would be for her mother.

According to Hindu values, white is the purist form of light. Her mother would need to wear white for the rest of her life.

Scott headed for the Indian High Commission. Remarkably, he got his visa the same day. The next morning, they headed for Heathrow early so as not to get caught in bad traffic. The bank provided a car for the two of them.

Fortunately, the flight was on time and landed in New Delhi without incident. They were at the Seshadri residence two hours after landing. Mrs. Seshadri, dressed in a white sari, was at Mrs. Choudhury's residence next door. Rakhi's mother was remarkably calm. Mother and daughter embraced. Scott was included. Rakhi told her mother all three of them would stay at the nearby Asoka hotel in a suite they had booked.

The next day, the service began at the Seshadri residence. A simple coffin was laid on the dining room table, surrounded by flowers. It was open, and Mr. Seshadri looked peaceful and as much in command as though he were still among the living.

There were only immediate neighbors and a few close friends in attendance. There were no living family members. It was an honor that Scott, a non-Hindu, participated, thanks to the graciousness of his mother-in-law. The traditional ceremony lasted less than two hours, and then they returned to Mrs. Choudhury's residence for a gathering that included curry and rice.

The cremation of the body occurred the next day, and Scott booked a flight for all three of them to go to Varanasi, the holy city on the Ganges River, so that the ashes could be immersed in the sacred river. They stayed the night in the modern tourist hotel near the Varanasi airport.

On the morning of the immersion of the ashes, the three journeyed into the old portion of the city and walked down the steps, known as ghats, to the river's edge. Scott commissioned a boat to take them out into the middle of the river, from where Mrs. Seshadri opened the lid of the vessel and dispersed the ashes into the river.

Mrs. Seshadri felt she properly had done her duty, her dharma, for her departed husband's soul. He could reside in peace until he began again the journey of life. He had been a good man who had lived with honor and done his duty to the Gods and to his family. Scott cried for the old man, as did his daughter.

Back in New Delhi, there was still the traditional ten days that had to be observed by the traditions of Hinduism. Rakhi and her mother spent the days principally with Mrs. Choudhury, while Scott generally remained in the hotel suite, reading, and thereafter in a fit of inspiration, composing a feature story for his newspaper on what he had seen in the holy city of Varanasi.

Chapter Eleven

A Hope for a New Beginning

On the final evening in New Delhi before departing for the London-bound flight, Scott and Rakhi were alone at the Asoka Hotel. It was not lost on either one of them that it was at this hotel that their life in London had started ten years earlier.

"Remember how we wanted a honeymoon in Paris?" asked Scott in a pensive mood.

"Yes," replied Rakhi, lost in her own thoughts. Then she added, "We had high hopes then. Did they come true?"

"Of course," replied Scott instantly. Then he too added, "You know, this hotel and this neighborhood have been a major part of our lives together. Remember how I plotted to join you and your father as he took his 'constitutional' every evening on the residential streets nearby?"

Scott added, "I thought you were the most beautiful woman I had ever seen, and I had to meet you somehow."

Rakhi added, "You were such an earnest young man. Even my father approved of your manner, although he commented occasionally that you were more than a bit naïve and needed seasoning. I guess you got that along the way."

"You mean, he actually approved of me all along?" asked Scott.

"Yes, of course. Had he not, you would never have had a chance to court me."

Returning to her earlier question, Scott elaborated on Rakhi's question about how life had turned out for them in these ensuing ten years. "You have been successful beyond your wildest dreams. You are a force to be reckoned with in your office, and I know much greater management responsibility is going to come to you sooner than you think."

Rakhi replied wistfully, "Well, it has been a good run, but the price has been high. We are not the young and blissfully in love couple we were then."

Scott was stung hard by her candor. "I love you as much as ever. We just need to plan our lives so that we can be together more often and become close again personally."

"Yes, I agree. It's worth a try. Can't give up now," Rakhi allowed, but not too convincingly.

He cast thoughts of Nasreen aside. "I have an idea! Why don't we take a couple of days personally before we head back to London? We could stop in Paris and stay a few nights again at the Plaza Athénée."

"And do what?" she asked.

"Pop champagne corks off the balcony and make love again."

Rakhi sighed, "Oh, those days are probably over. I don't think I can recapture that carefree mood again."

Scott insisted, "I'm going to make hotel and flight reservations first thing tomorrow morning. You'll see. It will be good, very good."

"Okay," she allowed, kissing him gently for his youthful enthusiasm and optimism.

Epilogue

"When death comes and whispers to me,
"Thy days are ended,"
Let me say to him, I have lived in love
And not in mere time."
He will ask, "Will thy songs remain?"
I shall say, "I know not, but this I know
That often when I sang I found my eternity."

RABINDRANATH TAGORE
1913 Nobel Prize for Literature
Composed in English and one of his "Fireflies" poems

In recent years, those who have heard some of the stories from my youth, (but certainly not all recorded in this memoir), have asked what happened upon Rakhi's and my return to London and where was Rakhi, since I am alone in my seventies teaching at Sweetbriar College.

There are many more adventures to record of our lives together, and I may tell those stories someday. But to answer a few questions, Rakhi and I returned to London from New Delhi in 1990 after Rakhi's father's death, and we continued there for some years, she at the bank and I at the newspaper office.

Rakhi had a change of heart about raising a child, although a baby did not arise to us in the normal course of events. Ever practical, Rakhi suggested adopting. Like a miracle, an infant became available from Pakistan, a little girl found at the Lahore Railway Station. We brought her back to London. She was a delight.

Rakhi's natural empathy and affection made her a superb mother. Rakhi's own mother moved from New Delhi to live with us, and she accepted the new little one from Lahore and took it as her duty to raise the child as a proper Hindu.

One day, a recruiting agent for a large American bank contacted Rakhi about a move to New York. He mentioned very senior responsibilities could be Rakhi's for the asking. We made the plunge, buying a big house in Connecticut. Rakhi's mother came along, of course.

It wasn't long after the move to Connecticut that I gave up journalism for a combination of part-time teaching at a local college, writing fiction, and staying close to home.

Rakhi died suddenly of pancreatic cancer some years ago. Fortunately, our daughter was grown and could cope, a bit, with the loss of her mother. Mrs. Seshadri, a kind soul, is gone too, and fortunately did not have to see her daughter pass on before she did. I firmly believe that Mrs. Seshadri did her duty toward raising a new child, as she had so properly done with Rakhi, and that she has found peace wherever she is now.

Author's Profile

Stephen E. Eisenbraun is a retired Foreign Service Officer whose assignments overseas included Bangladesh, Pakistan, Sierra Leone, and Kenya. His Washington assignments included, among other offices, the India desk, the Tunisia desk, and the combined Kenya and Uganda desks. Eisenbraun was a political officer during tumultuous times in South Asia when India, Pakistan, and Bangladesh experienced political turmoil, including an Air Force mutiny in Bangladesh and the burning of the U.S. Embassy in Pakistan. Eisenbraun was Deputy Chief of Mission in Sierra Leone and Principal Officer/Consul in Mombasa, Kenya.

In Washington, Eisenbraun also worked on the staff of the Senate Foreign Relations Committee.

Prior to joining the Foreign Service, Eisenbraun studied Hindi at Delhi University in India under the auspices of a fellowship from the American Institute of Indian Studies. He has a master's degree in International Relations from the Johns Hopkins University's School of Advanced International Studies.

In retirement, Eisenbraun continues to work as a consultant to the Department of State as the Editor in Chief of the Department's annual *Country Reports on Human Rights*. He is a past Chairman of the Editorial Board of the *Foreign Service Journal*.

Danger and Romance in Foreign Lands

To see the world, to report political intrigue and corruption abroad, to take the gifts of white privilege and freedom as an American citizen and do something worthwhile—these are the ambitions of Scott Higgins, a young American foreign correspondent in South Asia who becomes caught up in dramatic political events in Bangladesh and Pakistan in the 1970s. It is in India that he also makes an unexpected connection with Rakhi, a smart, savvy, and sultry woman who is also a banking professional. Together Scott and Rakhi move to Nairobi, where, even as newlyweds, their lives and welfare are seriously threatened in the exotic country of Kenya. Later, after an extravagant honeymoon in Paris, their last assignment is in London, where Rakhi's career blossoms, but not without its severe troubles.